Handling data

Brombol

KEY STAGE
TWO

PHOTOCOPIABLES

impact

MATHS HOMEWORK

Published by Scholastic Publications Ltd,
Villiers House,
Clarendon Avenue,
Leamington Spa,
Warwickshire CV32 5PR

Reprinted 1994

UNIVERSITY OF
NORTH LONDON

Activities by the IMPACT Project
at the University of North London,
collated and rewritten by Ruth
Merttens and Ros Leather

Editor Jo Saxelby-Jennings
Assistant editor Joanne Boden
Designer Tracey Ramsey
Series designer Anna Oliwa
Illustrations Gloria
Cover illustration Anna Oliwa

Designed using Aldus Pagemaker
Processed by Salvo Print and Design
Artwork by Pages Bureau, Leamington Spa

Printed in Great Britain
by Clays Ltd, St Ives plc

British Library Cataloguing-in-Publication Data
A catalogue record for this book is
available from the British Library.

ISBN 0-590-53158-1

Handling data

impact
C O N T E N T S

Handling data

impact
CONTENTS

impact
INTRODUCTION

This series of IMPACT books is designed to help you run a non-traditional homework scheme. Through the use of take-home maths activities, children can share maths with a parent/carer in the context of the home. The results of these activities then feed back into the classwork at school.

IMPACT works through the following processes:
● Teachers plan their maths for the next few weeks as usual and consider which parts might usefully be done at home.
● Teachers look through selected activities which fit in with what they are planning.
● The activities are photocopied and sent home with the children every week or fortnight.
● The results of each activity are brought back into the classroom by the children and form part of the following week's classwork.

In practice this process will be slightly different in each classroom and in each school. Teachers may adapt it to fit their own way of working and the ethos of the school. Most schools send out IMPACT activities fortnightly, although some do send it weekly. There is some evidence to suggest that weekly activities get a slightly better response and help to raise standards more effectively than

fortnightly, but this is not conclusive. The important point is that each teacher should feel comfortable with how often the IMPACT activities are used in his or her class.

Planning

When you, the teacher, are looking at your work and deciding what maths, roughly speaking, you plan to be doing over the next few weeks, all that is necessary is to consider which parts may usefully be done or practised at home. It is helpful if, over a period of time, a variety of activities are chosen. These tend to fall into three broad categories:
● Activities which practise a skill – these are useful in that they can be followed up in the routine classwork the children are doing. They must be carefully selected by the teacher according to the level of the children.
● Activities which collect data – these lead into work on data-handling and representation.
● Activities in which children measure or make something – this produces an object or some measurements to be used later in class.

The activities in this book are divided into four sections according to age: Year 3, Year 4, Year 5 and Year 6. There are two pages of teachers' notes relating to the individual activities at the beginning of each section. Links to National Curriculum attainment targets are included in the teachers' notes and numerals in brackets refer to the programmes of study, so AT 2/1 (iii, iv) refers to Attainment Target 2, Level 1, Programmes of Study 3 and 4. Details of how these relate to the curricula in Scotland and Northern Ireland are given on page 128.

Working with parents

It is important for the success of IMPACT that the activities taken home are seen by the parents to be maths. We always suggest, at least until IMPACT is up and running and parents' confidence in it is well established, that activities are chosen which have a clearly mathematical purpose. Save the more 'wacky' activities until later! You will get a much better response if parents believe that what they are doing is maths.

Each activity contains a note to parents which explains the purpose of the activity and how they can best help. It also gives a reference to National Curriculum attainment targets – although not to any level. Teachers who prefer not to have these can white them out. The IMPACT activities should be accompanied by an IMPACT diary, enabling parents and children to make their comments. See page 128 for details.

Making the most of IMPACT

The quickest way to reduce the number of children who share the maths at home is to ignore or be negative about the work they bring back into school. When they come running into the classroom, tripping over the string which went twice round their cat, it is difficult to welcome them all individually but it is crucial that the activities done at home are followed up in classwork. The nature and type of this follow-up depends very much upon the nature of the activity, and specific suggestions are made in the teachers' notes. However, some general points apply:
● Number activities, such as games, can often be repeated in a more formalised way in the classwork. For example, if the children have been playing a dice game, throwing two dice and adding the totals, they can continue to do this in the

classroom, but this time they can record all the 'sums' in their maths book. This applies to any skills-practice activity.
● Data-collecting activities, of any description, need to be followed up by allowing the children to work together in small groups to collate, analyse and represent their joint data. This will inevitably involve children in a discussion as to how their data was obtained, and any problems they encountered while obtaining it.
● If the children have made or measured something at home, the information or the object needs to be used as part of the classwork. This will not be too difficult since this type of activity is selected by the teacher precisely in order to provide the measurements or shapes for use in class.

The implication of this is that it is wise to select a variety of activities to send home. No teacher wants to drown in data, nor do they want all the IMPACT activities to result in more routine number work. Some activities generate lots of follow-up work while others simply require minimal follow-up – perhaps just a discussion about who won and who lost, and how many times people played the game.

Many of the activities can lead to an attractive display or enable the teacher to make a class book. Such a book does not have to be 'grand'. It can be simply five or six large sheets of sugar paper folded in the middle and stitched/stapled with the children's work mounted inside it. The children love these books, and they make a fine record of their work. An IMPACT display board in the school entrance hall gives parents a sense that their work at home is appreciated.

For further details of IMPACT see page 128.

Teachers' Notes
YEAR THREE

Colour chart The children can share their graphs or charts. How many examples of each different colour did they find? Working in groups, they can collate their data on to one large graph. Which colours seem to be most common? What colours occur most frequently in our environment? Talk about this.
National Curriculum: AT 1/3 (i, ii); AT 5/2 (ii)

Initial sort Put all the information together and construct a large graph with all the letters of the alphabet. Which letters got left out? Can they fill in these in the classroom? Which letters were hard and which were easy?
National Curriculum: AT 1/3 (i, ii); AT 5/2 (ii)

Furniture count-up The children will need to discuss in class what categories they found. Do many items of furniture fit in two categories; for example, wood and fabric? How could they be displayed on a chart? Let the children work in groups to make a large block graph of all the different types of furniture – chairs, tables, fridges and so on. Perhaps each of the groups could be concerned with a different room in the house – depending upon which room the children chose to survey?
National Curriculum: AT 1/2 (ii); AT 5/2 (i)

Relation hunt The children can work in groups and make one large Venn diagram with all their relations on it. They could draw pictures of them all! Can they also make a block graph showing where their relations live? What places would they need to include?
National Curriculum: AT 1/2 (i, ii); AT 5/3 (i, iv)

Weekday television With the whole class, discuss the programmes they have found. Which ones did everybody find and which ones got left out? Do some more work using the TV schedules. What types of programme can the children find? How can they be categorised? Draw a block graph of the various types.
National Curriculum: AT 1/2 (i, ii); AT 5/3 (i)

Crazy characters Create a card database in the classroom. The children must transfer all their information on to cards, with the name in the top left-hand corner. They can paste on their pictures. How should the cards be arranged? Discuss how information can be accessed. Suppose you want to select all those characters who were born before a certain date, how could you do this? Perhaps move on to using a computer database.
National Curriculum: AT 1/3 (i); 5/3 (ii)

Technology survey Discuss with the children the difficulties of defining what is meant by 'technology'. Try to come up with an agreed definition. Then consider the categories into which the various examples of technology can be divided. Working in groups, the children could devise these categories and represent their data on a graph.
National Curriculum: AT 1/3 (i, ii); AT 5/3 (iv)

Housework survey How would the children suggest representing this data? It could be a pie chart or a block graph, showing what percentage of the housework is done by mums, by dads, by older or younger brothers or sisters and so on. How are they going to decide in each case? If mum does the washing and dad takes out the rubbish, are they doing equal work? Talk about what they have found out.
National Curriculum: AT 1/3 (i, ii); AT 5/3 (iv)

Meal survey The children can categorise their meals under generic headings, for example 'fish and chips', 'spagetti bolognese' and so on and then create a block graph showing the numbers of people for whom each one is their favourite meal. Are there some meals which are liked by only a few people? Which meals are healthy and which meals are not so good for us?
National Curriculum: AT 1/3 (ii); AT 5/2 (i, ii, iii)

Car number plates The children can try adding up all the numbers in their list. (They may need to use a calculator!) Whose list adds up to the largest number? Categorise the number plates according to agreed criteria such as by year of registration; for example, all plates that start with K and so on. Make a block graph of the results. How old are most of the cars around the neighbourhood?
National Curriculum: AT 1/2 (i); AT 2/2 (ii); AT 5/3 (iv)

Where would you like to live?
The children can work in groups and put together their information on to one large graph. Discuss the categories. Do some of them overlap? Is it difficult to find suitable headings? Perhaps you can make one large class graph, or mount all their group graphs in a class book.
National Curriculum: AT 1/3 (i, ii); AT 5/3 (iv)

Hopping graph The children can collate all their results into one large chart. What was the most and least number of hops? Did more than one person do the same number? Discuss what is the best way of representing this information. How large will the graph be?
National Curriculum: AT 1/3 (i, ii); AT 5/3 (iv)

Crisp survey The children can collate all their information on to a large chart with all the brand names down one side and the numbers of crisps written beside them. What happens if two children found different numbers of crisps for the same brand? Talk about averages. Which is the best buy? Is it necessarily the packet with the most in?
National Curriculum: AT 1/3 (i, ii); AT 5/3 (iv)

TV personalities The children will need to discuss their categories. Do they agree on them? Then you can collate the information on to one large class graph. Are most personalities male or female? Adults or children? Human or not?
National Curriculum AT 1/3 (i, ii); AT 5/3 (iv)

Film memories Working in groups, the children can collate their data on to charts – how many of each type of film have they seen? These charts can then be used to make one large class graph. Which type of film proves most popular? This work quite naturally feeds into a computer database.
National Curriculum: AT 1/2 (ii); AT 5/2 (iii)

Bug search Working in groups the children can collate their data on to charts – how many of each type of creature have they seen? How can these creatures best be categorised? These charts can then feed into a computer database and the children can then decide how to represent the data.
National Curriculum: AT 1/2 (ii); AT 5/3 (iii)

Watch watch! The children can enter their data on to a simple computer database. They can then decide how they want the data represented, and also what questions they wish to put to it. Alternatively, the children can collate all their information on to one large chart and then on to a graph.
National Curriculum: AT 1/3 (i, ii); AT 5/3 (iii, iv)

Computer survey The children can discuss their findings. How do they want to represent their data? They may find that a Venn diagram answers their need, or even a Carroll diagram, or they may decide upon a chart or graph.
National Curriculum: AT 1/3 (i, ii); AT 5/3 (iv)

Children's TV The children can collate their data and decide on the categories that they think are appropriate. Working in small groups, they can enter the data into a simple computer database. They can then think about how to represent what they have found out.
National Curriculum: AT 1/3 (i, ii); AT 5/3 (iii, iv)

Addition survey The children can discuss all the different ways of doing the sums. Were some of them always done in the same way? Did the people surveyed find some harder than others? What were the times taken? Can the children classify the responses and represent them on a graph?
National Curriculum: AT 1/3 (i, ii); AT 2/2 (i, iii); AT 3/3 (i); AT 5/3 (iv)

Dicey deal The children can play the games in pairs in class, recording all their throws. They can then collate the information obtained by several of the pairs. How many times was the dice thrown in all? How many of the throws were sixes, how many were twos and so on. Should it make any difference which number you choose if the dice is fair? Talk about the chances of throwing any number.
National Curriculum: AT 1/2 (i, ii); AT 2/3 (ii); AT 5/3 (v)

Turn up for the books The children can discuss how close they got to the page that they guessed. Their results can be recorded on a graph according to how close they were to the actual page; that is, how many children got the actual page, how many got within one page and so on. What do the children think are their chances of getting the actual page – good, not very good or poor?
National Curriculum: AT 1/3 (i, ii); AT 2/3 (iv); AT 5/3 (v, vi)

Spinning Jenny! The children can discuss how they coloured their particular tracks and why they did it in that way. What were their criteria? How did they decide how many spaces to colour in each colour and how to position them? Does it make any difference? If the tracks were coloured in only two colours, would it make it harder to get to the end? Would it make it harder to win? Ask the children to design their own spinners and track games.
National Curriculum: AT 1/3 (i, ii); AT 5/3 (v, vi)

Card in my pocket The children can play this game in class and discuss their strategies. Is it sensible to wait until you have whittled down the choices to two or three cards? What are your chances of being right then? What are your chances of being right if you guess straight away?
National Curriculum: AT 1/3 (ii); AT 5/3 (v, vi)

Turn it over The children can play this game in school, scoring the value of the coin under the card at each 'wrong' guess. This will help practise arithmetic skills. Discuss the chances of being right first time. How much easier does it get to be right with subsequent guesses, and why?
National Curriculum: AT 1/3 (i, ii); AT 5/3 (v, vi)

Trial and error The children can play this game again in class and record all their throws. When they collate all their results, what do they notice? How many throws did they have in all? How many times did a player get two right in a row? How many times did they get three right in a row? What conclusions can the children draw about the possibilities involved (the children do not need to calculate the precise probabilities here – just get an idea of the direction in which the likelihood is moving – that is, it is getting more or less likely!)
National Curriculum: AT 1/3 (i, ii); AT 5/3 (v, vi, vii)

Coin shuffle The children can play this game in pairs in class. Discuss their strategies for predicting how many heads and tails there will be. What is a sensible prediction? What is a foolhardy one? Record all their throws and collate the data to show which layouts are more likely.
National Curriculum: AT 1/3 (i, ii); AT 5/3 (v, vi, vii)

Roll a penny The children can compare their starting positions. Do they think they were all fair? What criteria determined their choice? Discuss the chances of the penny landing on a particular space – are all the spaces equally likely?
National Curriculum: AT 1/3 (ii); AT 5/3 (v, vi, vii)

Likely sayings The children can compare their words and phrases. There should, of course, be a degree of consensus about the expressions and words in current use among the children themselves. Display these in one set. Then a second set could collate the children's data as to the words and phrases in current use among adults. Is there any consensus here? Finally, what about those which have now dated? Make a set of these, collating the children' information. How probable is it that the children will hear a certain word or phrase in five minutes of conversation in the playground? Can they find out?
National Curriculum: AT 1/2 (ii); AT 5/2 (ii, v)

Matching a dice How likely are the children to throw a six? What are the chances of two sixes in a row? The children can play this again in class and talk about the probabilities involved. Suppose we had two sets of cards (1–6), would this make the game easier or harder? What would be your chances of turning over a six then?
National Curriculum: AT 1/3 (ii); AT 5/3 (v, vi)

_____and

child

_____

helper(s)

_____

did this activity together

Colour chart

● Look around the room.

● How many examples of each colour can you find?

For example: if you can see a blue cushion, a blue lampshade, a blue stripe on the wallpaper, some blue books and a blue vase, this counts as five examples of blue.

Find examples of as many colours as you can.

● Complete this chart or graph, putting the colours along the bottom and colouring in blocks above each one.

● Bring your chart/graph into school.

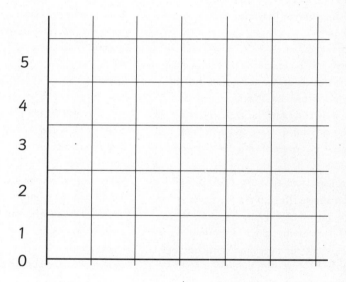

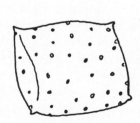

impact MATHS HOMEWORK

Initial sort

● What is the initial letter of your name? Write it down here.

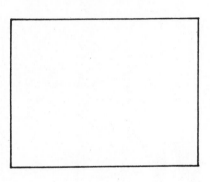

● Have a hunt for as many things as you can find around your home which begin with your initial.

● How many can you find?

● Make a list of them below.

● Can you arrange them in different categories – for example: edible, non-edible, alive, not alive and so on.

● Make a chart or a graph to display your information. Bring it into school.

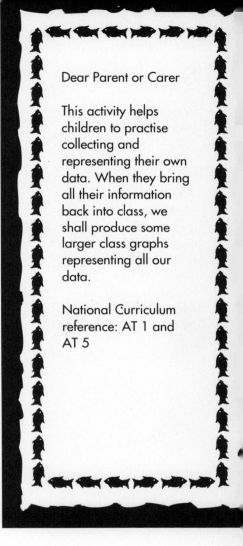

_____and

child

_____

helper(s)

_____

did this activity together

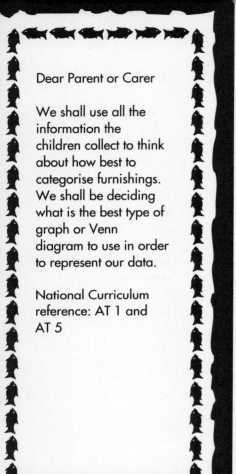
_____and

child

_____

helper(s)

_____

did this activity together

Furniture count-up

● Look around a room in your home and make a list of all the different items of furniture you can see.

● Make a note of what each item is made from using the following categories: wood, metal, plastic, cloth/fabric. If you can think of any other categories, use those as well.

● Bring your list into school.

impact MATHS HOMEWORK

Relation hunt

● How many relations do you have? Are they male or female, old or young, living near or living far away?

● Write the names of as many relations as you can on to the Venn diagram below, making sure you get them in the right sets. (You do not have to state their relationship to you – if you want, you can include 'aunties' who aren't really aunties, and next-door neighbours who act as 'grandads'!)

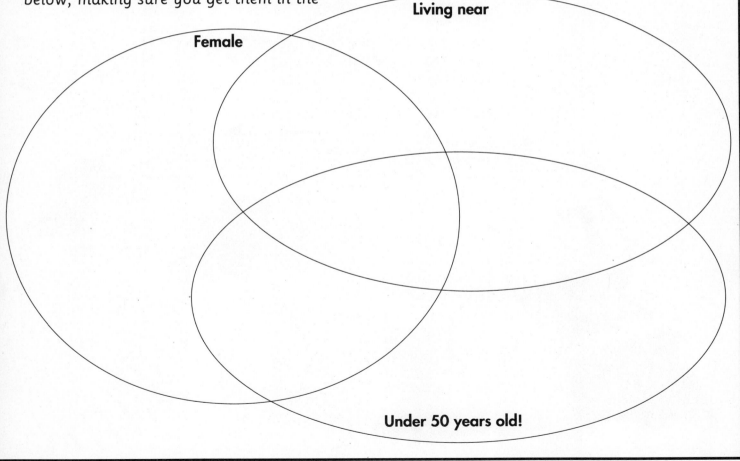

Female

Living near

Under 50 years old!

Dear Parent or Carer

In class, we shall collate all our information on to one large Venn diagram and then discuss other ways of representing and analysing our data.

National Curriculum reference: AT 1 and AT 5

_____and

child

_____

helper(s)

_____

did this activity together

_____and

child

_____

helper(s)

_____

did this activity together

Weekday television

YOU WILL NEED: a newspaper with the television schedules in it, a pencil and paper.

● Can you find any programmes which are on every weekday?

● Make a list below of all those that you find. Make sure you check every channel.

● Bring your lists into school.

impact MATHS HOMEWORK

Crazy characters

We are making a database at school of 'Crazy characters'. We need the vital statistics of all the characters who will be entered into it.

● Design three characters for our database.

For each character, you must supply: a picture (of either the face or of the whole person); his or her date of birth, age, country of birth, and a brief biography (story of his or her life). This last item should be no longer than 30 words.

● Bring all your characters into school.

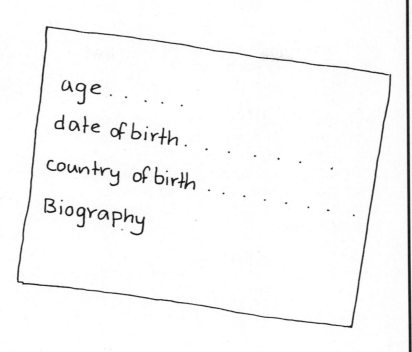

age . . . . .

date of birth . . . .

country of birth . . . .

Biography

Dear Parent or Carer

We are creating a database at school and the children will enter, access and retrieve information from this base. This is part of their work in data handling.

National Curriculum reference: AT 1 and AT 5

_____and

child

_____

helper(s)

_____

did this activity together

_____and

child

_____

helper(s)

_____

did this activity together

Technology search

Is there too much technology in our daily lives? Are we hemmed in by faceless machines?!

● This weekend, look around you and make a note of every instance of what you would call 'technology' that you can find. Include obvious things like the washing machine, and not-so-obvious things like the machine that stamps pre-paid letters.

● Write everything you think of on to the Venn diagram below.

● Bring it back into school.

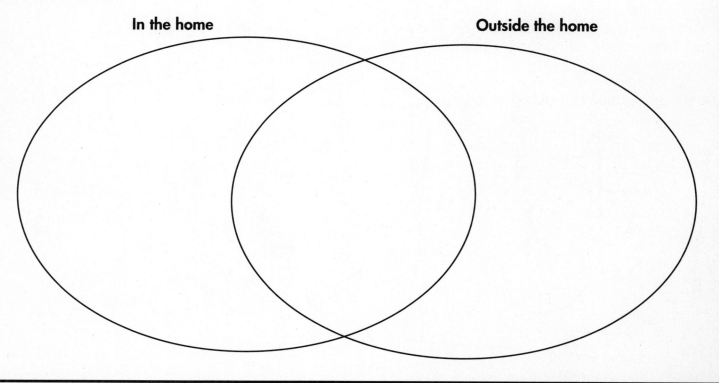

In the home   Outside the home

Housework survey

Who does all the housework in your house?

● Make a list below of all the household jobs that have to be done every day or every week. Don't forget to include things like 'taking the rubbish out' and 'cleaning the rabbit hutch'.

● Put the names of the person or people who mainly do those jobs beside them.

● Bring your lists back into school.

Dear Parent or Carer

All the information which the children collect in this survey will be analysed and represented on a graph as a part of our work on handling data.

National Curriculum reference: AT 1 and AT 5

_____and

child

_____

helper(s)

_____

did this activity together

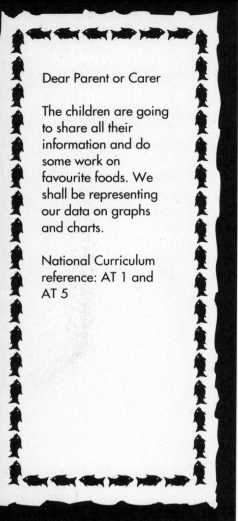
_____and

child

_____

helper(s)

_____

did this activity together

Meal survey

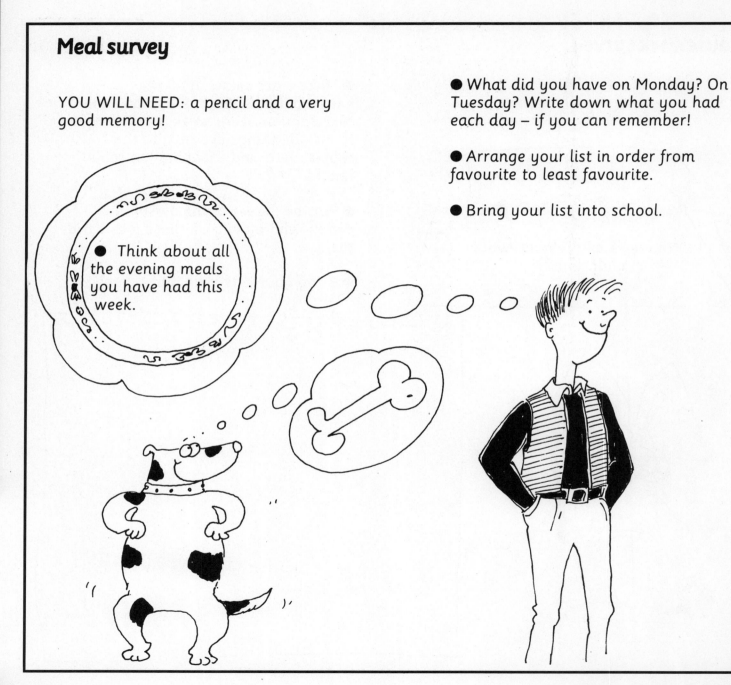

YOU WILL NEED: a pencil and a very good memory!

● Think about all the evening meals you have had this week.

● What did you have on Monday? On Tuesday? Write down what you had each day – if you can remember!

● Arrange your list in order from favourite to least favourite.

● Bring your list into school.

impact MATHS HOMEWORK

Car number plates

Some car number plates look pretty funny, others look boring.

● Do your own car number plates survey. With a helper, copy at least ten number plates from around and about your neighbourhood.

● Write them down in a list below.

● Are there some letters which turn up again and again?

● Bring your lists into school.

Dear Parent or Carer

The children are going to use these numbers for a great deal of arithmetic work. We are also going to classify the number plates and use them in our data-handling work.

National Curriculum reference: AT 1, AT 2 and AT 5

_____and

child

_____

helper(s)

_____

did this activity together

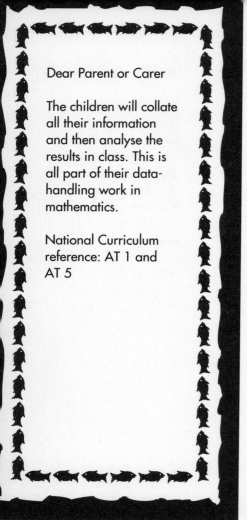
_____and

child

_____

helper(s)

_____

did this activity together

Where would you like to live?

Many people feel that they couldn't live anywhere other than a large city; others prefer the countryside.

● Devise a survey of where the people in your family say they would like to live. Decide on the categories you will give them to choose from – for example: large city centre, suburb, countryside, small town, largish town and so on.

● Then draw a small graph of your results.

Hopping graph

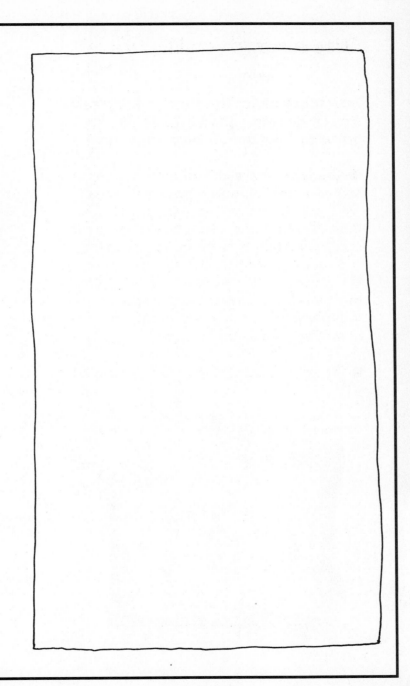

● How many times can you hop up and down on one leg before you topple over? Ask as many people as you can persuade to try this.

● Record how many times they each hop.

● Draw a graph showing how many times everyone you asked hopped.

Dear Parent or Carer

We shall be drawing a huge class graph which has all the figures that we have collected. This is part of our work on statistics and data handling.

National Curriculum reference: AT 1 and AT 5

_____and

child

_____

helper(s)

_____

did this activity together

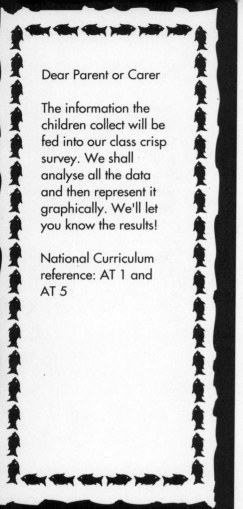

_____and

child

_____

helper(s)

_____

did this activity together

Crisp survey

How many crisps are there in a packet? Does it depend on the brand? We are going to conduct our own crisp survey.

● At some time over the weekend, ask someone to buy you a packet of crisps.

● Use a plate and count the crisps carefully on to it before you eat them!

● How many were there? Write down the brand name, the price and the number of crisps. (Don't count the crumbled bits in the bottom!)

● Bring your information into school.

TV personalities

How many TV personalities are there? Are they mostly women or men? Boys or girls? Animals? Cartoon characters?

● Make a chart or graph below of all the TV personalities you and your family can think of.

● Categorise them under the headings given and any others you can think of.

● How many are there in each column?

● Which one is your favourite?

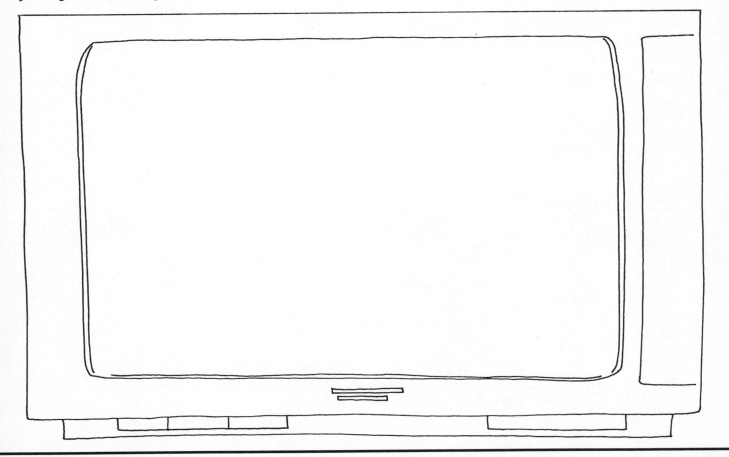

Dear Parent or Carer

We shall put together all our information on to one large graph. We shall be discussing the categories and whether any of these are problematic. This is all part of our classwork on data handling.

National Curriculum reference: AT 1 and AT 5

_____and

child

_____

helper(s)

_____

did this activity together

_____and

child

_____

helper(s)

_____

did this activity together

Film memories

Have you been to the cinema or
watched films at home on the TV
or video?

● Can you remember the last three
films you saw? Ask someone to help
you.

● Write down their names and use
some of the following words to describe
each one:

adventure;
disaster film;
science-fiction film;
action film;
western;
historical film;
cartoon;
romance;
comedy.

● Draw a picture to illustrate your
favourite film.

impact MATHS HOMEWORK

Bug search

● How many insects, spiders and the like can you see in one weekend?!

● Keep a tally of all the bugs you see under different headings, such as spiders, woodlice, flies, moths and so on.

● Bring your lists into school.

Dear Parent or Carer

This activity is part of a survey we are doing in school. The children will collate, analyse and represent their data on a graph.

National Curriculum reference: AT 1 and AT 5

_____and

child

_____

helper(s)

_____

did this activity together

Watch watch!

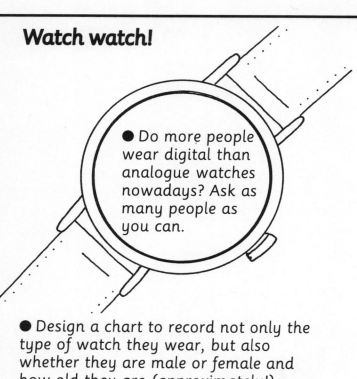

● Do more people wear digital than analogue watches nowadays? Ask as many people as you can.

● Design a chart to record not only the type of watch they wear, but also whether they are male or female and how old they are (approximately!).

● Bring all your information into class.

Computer survey

How many of your friends, relations and acquaintances have a computer?

● Conduct your own survey to find out.

● Make a chart showing the number of people you asked and their answers. Include on your chart a space for recording whether the computer is used primarily for work or for playing games and note whether the person is male or female.

● Bring all your findings into school.

Dear Parent or Carer

We shall use this information to do some work in the mathematical area of handling data and representing it graphically. The children may well enter this data on to a simple computer database.

National Curriculum reference: AT 1 and AT 5

_____and

child

_____

helper(s)

_____

did this activity together

_____ and

child

_____

helper(s)

did this activity together

Children's TV

● How many children's TV programmes do you regularly watch in a week? We are only counting the programmes which are broadcast as part of children's television.

● Make a list of all the programmes you watch regularly. Decide what headings to list the programmes under – for example: comedy, adventure, cartoon and so on.

● Bring your lists into school.

impact MATHS HOMEWORK

Addition survey

● How do most people do addition sums? Give as many people as you can the following four sums to do:

3 + 18 =

100 + 1000 =

76 + 68 =

39 + 29 =

● Record how long (roughly) they take to do the sums and what method they use – pencil and paper (be sure to offer them this!), in their heads, with a calculator and so on. Try to get each person to note down the method they used, such as 'Adding the tens, then the units, …'.

● Bring all the results of your survey into school.

Dear Parent or Carer

We shall use this information for a data-handling exercise, classifying and analysing the various methods used. However, we shall also use it to help us to practise our own addition!

National Curriculum reference: AT 1, AT 2, AT 3 and AT 5

_____and

child

_____

helper(s)

_____

did this activity together

_____and

child

_____

helper(s)

_____

did this activity together

Dicey deal

YOU WILL NEED: a dice, paper and a pencil.

● You and your helper should each choose a number between 1 and 6 inclusive.

● Take it in turns to throw the dice. Each player starts with a score of 12 points. If you throw your chosen number score 10 points. If you throw any other number lose 2 points.

● Play until either someone is down to 0 points, or someone is up to 50 points!

● Play again with a different number each. Does it make any difference which number you choose?

Turn up for the books

● What is your chance of opening a book at a particular page?

● Choose a book. Not one which is hundreds of pages long, but one which has about 50 pages.

● Decide what page you are going to try to open it at. Write your guess down below.

● Open the book. What page did you get? Write it down below and score the difference between the two numbers.

● Let someone else have a turn. Have three goes each. Write your scores on the back of this sheet.

● Add up your scores – lowest wins!

● Bring all your scores back into school.

_____and

child

_____

helper(s)

_____

did this activity together

Dear Parent or Carer

We are working on the mathematical area of probability and this game will help us to work out the odds of obtaining a particular outcome.

National Curriculum reference: AT 1 and AT 5

_____and

child

_____

helper(s)

_____

did this activity together

Spinning Jenny!

● Cut out the spinner at the bottom of the page and stick it on the back of an old Christmas or birthday card.

● Cut round it and colour in each of the segments in a different colour.

● Colour in the track on the accompanying page in such a way that you can spin the spinner and move along the track according to the colour indicated on the spinner. Colour it so that it is fair!

● Now play the game with someone. Who wins?

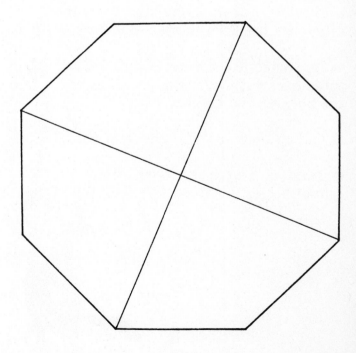

Spinning Jenny!

_____and

child

_____

helper(s)

_____

did this activity together

Card in my pocket

YOU WILL NEED: a pack of cards with the face (picture) cards and the numbers below 5 removed.

● Deal out five cards to yourself and five cards to your opponent. Put the rest in a pile face down in the middle.

● Each player looks at their cards and spreads them out face down on the table in front of them.

● The players each then put one card from these five 'in their pockets' (or behind them). They must not show them to the other player.

● Now take it in turns to take a card from the pile.

● Turn it face up in the middle of the table beside the pile. Lay each subsequent card next to the previous one so that they can all be seen.

● At any point a player can try to guess what card is in his or her opponent's pocket. BUT every time you guess incorrectly, you must turn over one of your other four cards.

● The first person to guess the card in the other player's pocket is the winner.

impact MATHS HOMEWORK

Turn it over

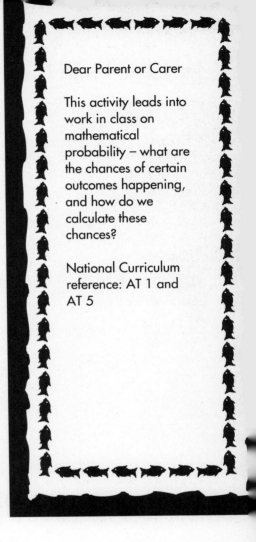

Dear Parent or Carer

This activity leads into work in class on mathematical probability – what are the chances of certain outcomes happening, and how do we calculate these chances?

National Curriculum reference: AT 1 and AT 5

YOU WILL NEED: some cards and some coins.

● Shut your eyes. Ask someone to lay out six cards with six different coins underneath them.

● Now guess which coin is under which card. Each time you make a guess (such as, 'The six of hearts is over the 50p.') you will score 5 points.

● If your guess is correct – leave the coin exposed!

● If your guess is incorrect – cover the coin back up and score the number on the card as well!

● The aim is to guess all the coins with as low a score as possible.

● When all the coins are uncovered, lay the cards and coins out in a different way while the other person shuts their eyes. Now let them guess.

● Who wound up with the lowest score?

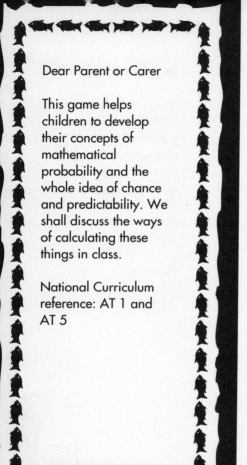
Trial and error

YOU WILL NEED: a coin, a pencil and paper.

● Take it in turns with your helper to throw the coin. Before you throw it guess whether it will land heads or tails.

● Score as follows:

If you are right, take 2 points;

If you are right twice in a row, take 4 points;

If you are right three times in a row, take 8 points;

If you are right four times in a row, take 16 points. And so on

● Play until one of you has more than 20 points.

● Play again. Do you think the scoring is fair?

Coin shuffle

YOU WILL NEED: five coins and a cup.

● Decide that one of you is 'heads' and the other is 'tails'.

● Take it in turns to put the coins in a cup and shake them out on to the table. Before you do this, predict how many heads there will be and how many tails.

● How do they land? If your prediction was correct, you may score the number of your chosen side thrown (that is, if you are 'heads', score the number of heads thrown – but only if your prediction was correct!).

● Keep playing until someone has reached a score of over 12 points. Who wins?

Dear Parent or Carer

This game directs the children's attention to various aspects of the mathematical study of probability. We are working on this in class at the moment.

National Curriculum reference: AT 1 and AT 5

_____and

child

_____

helper(s)

_____

did this activity together

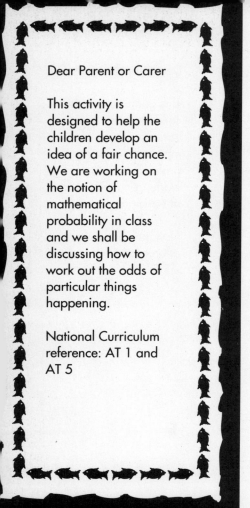
Roll a penny

● Using the tracks on the accompanying page, play the following game.

● Two people have to roll a penny along the page in order to get the highest score. They must do this at the same time. The space in which their penny lands determines the score. (The penny counts as being in a space if most of it is lying in that space!)

● Discuss how you can make the game fair by deciding from where you each have to roll your penny. Mark the starting positions on the page.

● Play several times, adding your scores as you go. Who wins?

● Are your starting positions fair?

● Bring your page back into school.

impact MATHS HOMEWORK

Roll a penny

score
4

score
8

score
7

score
5

_____and

child

_____

helper(s)

_____

did this activity together

Likely sayings

● Do certain people have certain phrases or sayings that you associate with them? Is there a particular expression or word that is in fashion right now that everyone uses?

● During the weekend, listen out for such expressions or sayings.

● In the first set, make a list of two or three words or phrases which people are likely to say, along with the person who uses them!

● In the second set, try to make a list of phrases or sayings which are no longer in current use.

"BACK IN THE OLD DAYS..."

● Ask a grown-up if they can remember what they said when they were young! What words did they use which they wouldn't be heard saying today?!

● Bring your lists into school.

Nowadays!

" _____ "

_____

Said by _____

" _____ "

_____

Said by _____

" _____ "

_____

Said by _____

Used to be!

" _____ "

_____

Said by _____

" _____ "

_____

Said by _____

" _____ "

_____

Said by _____

impact MATHS HOMEWORK

Matching a dice

YOU WILL NEED: a set of cards numbered 1–6 (these can be cut from the back of an old cereal packet or a Christmas card) and a dice.

● Lay the cards out face down.

● Take it in turns with someone to throw the dice and turn over a card. You are trying to turn over the same card as the number on the dice. If you do so, you may keep the card. If you don't, turn the card back over, face down, and pass the dice on to your opponent.

● The winner is the person whose cards add up to the most at the end.

Dear Parent or Carer

This activity does ask the children to practise some arithmetic, but its main purpose is that it helps us to develop some of the concepts in the study of mathematical probability which we are working on in class. How likely is your child to throw a six? What are the chances of two sixes in a row?

National Curriculum reference: AT 1 and AT 5

_____and

child

_____

helper(s)

_____

did this activity together

Teachers' Notes
YEAR FOUR

Phone number count-up The children can put together their numbers and represent them on a graph using the reduced number as the means of sorting the phone numbers. How else could you categorise phone numbers? How are they organised in the phone book?
National Curriculum: AT 1/3 (ii); AT 2/3 (ii); AT 5/3 (iv)

Breakfast survey The children will need to collate all their data. They can then either enter it into a simple computer database, or they can decide how best to represent this data on a class graph.
National Curriculum: AT 1/3 (i, ii); AT 5/3 (iii, iv)

Carbohydrate survey The children will need to collate all their data. Discuss what sorts of carbohydrate are common. Are there cultural patterns? Talk about a healthy diet. Strictly speaking, sugars are carbohydrates too. You may wish to discuss with the children whether to include these in your survey or to leave them out. The children can enter their data into a simple computer database or they can decide how best to represent this information on a class graph.
National Curriculum: AT 1/3 (i, ii); AT 5/3 (iii, iv)

Number counting The children will need to work in small groups and talk through how they arrived at their answers. Compare answers. Which one is correct? Would it make any difference if it was the '4' that was broken? Emphasise that the key to finding a correct answer lies in how your information is handled and presented.
National Curriculum: AT1/3 (i, ii, iv); 2/3 (i); 5/3 (ii)

Phone book The children will need to work in small groups comparing flow charts. Can they come up with an agreed process? Have a few phone books to hand for them to check out how to access the information.
National Curriculum: AT 1/3 (i, ii, iv); AT 5/3 (i)

Five ways The children will need to work in small groups and talk through how they arrived at their answers. Compare answers. Which one is correct? Does it make it much harder to increase the size of the number – that is, to 7? Or, once they have a way of recording their findings, can the children apply it to any number? Emphasise that the key to finding a correct answer lies in how your information is handled and presented.
National Curriculum: AT 1/3 (i, ii, iv); AT 2/3 (ii); AT 5/3 (ii)

Favourite pastimes The children can work in groups and create a graph showing all their favourite pastimes. Discuss how they will categorise these. Does playing with dolls go in a different category from playing with teddies? A great deal in data representation depends upon the decisions made about how to categorise the information.
National Curriculum: AT 1/3 (i, ii, iv); AT 2/3 (ii); AT 5/3 (ii)

Electrical apparatus The children need to collate all their data. They could do this by entering it on to a simple computer database. Discuss what they have found out. Also discuss the implications of this information. Is the most mechanised home necessarily the happiest home? Or the most comfortable? Are there some electrical items we do not really need?
National Curriculum: AT 1/3 (i, ii); AT 5/3 (iii, iv)

Phone call survey The children can discuss how many phone calls their homes get. Why do some get more than others? Do some parents work from home? Make a class graph showing the different numbers of phone calls by banding together particular amounts, for example 900–1000 phone calls per year, 1000–1100 per year and so on.
National Curriculum: AT 1/3 (i, ii); AT 2/3 (i); AT 5/4 (iii)

Letter count-up The children can share their data here. They can band together certain amounts of letters received, such as 50–60 letters per year, 60–70 letters per year and so on. How large do the bands need to be? What is the most and least frequent number received?
National Curriculum: AT 1/3 (i, ii); AT 5/4 (iii)

Subtraction survey Use the results of this survey to stimulate a discussion on the various methods of doing subtraction. Is it sensible to do all the sums given in the same way? Which ones are easier to do in our heads? The children can also classify and record their data about how people actually do these sums. Were some of them more commonly done using paper and pencil? Represent the information obtained using a

three set Venn diagram – done mentally, don[e] using paper and pencil, and done using calculator.
National Curriculum: AT 1/3 (i, ii, iv); AT 2/3 (iv); AT 5/3 (iv)

Getting up! The children can discuss at what times the people they asked got up. Why do some get up earlier than others? Do some parents work nights or early mornings? Make a class graph showing the different getting-up times by banding together particular time intervals, for example 7.00–7.30 am, 10.00–10.30 am and so on.
National Curriculum: AT 1/3 (i, ii); AT 5/4 (iii)

Sweatshirt survey The children need to colla[te] all their data. They could do this by entering i[t] on to a simple computer database. Discuss what they have found out. Also discuss the implications of this information. Is the best value sweatshirt necessarily the most expensive? Or the most comfortable? Does th[e] picture or brand name really matter?
National Curriculum: AT 1/3 (i, ii); AT 5/3 (iii, iv)

What do you read? The children can work in groups to create a graph showing all the things they read. Discuss how they categorise these. Does a comic go in a different categor[y] from a magazine? What about a journal? A great deal in data representation depends upon the decisions made about how to categorise the information.
National Curriculum: AT 1/3 (i, ii); AT 5/3 (iv)

Favourite sport The children can work in groups and create a graph showing all their favourite sports. Discuss how they categorise these. Create a large whole-class graph or a series of graphs of different types produced by groups of children working together.
National Curriculum: AT 1/3 (i, ii); AT 5/3 (iv)

Back-pack survey The children need to collate all their data. They could do this by entering it on to a simple computer database. Discuss what they have found out. Also discuss the implications of this information. What makes a good back-pack? Can they give a list of the criteria which makes a backpack both popular and good for its purpose.
National Curriculum: AT 1/3 (i, ii); AT 5/3 (iii, iv)

Fruit and vegetables Check that the children have realised where on the diagram to write the fruit and vegetables that they did not like! The children can collect all their information together on to one enormous Venn diagram. Can they also represent what they have found out on a Carroll diagram?
National Curriculum: AT 1/3 (i, ii); AT 5/2 (iv)

Cat survey The children can work in groups and create a graph showing the numbers of cats they spotted. Discuss how they categorise these. Are the cats classified by colour or size? A great deal in data representation depends upon the decisions made about how to categorise the information. Finally, create a large whole-class graph.
National Curriculum: AT 1/3 (i, ii); AT 5/3 (iv)

Teddy distance The children can compare the lengths that their teddies 'flew'. Working in groups they can construct a graph to show the different lengths. They can then make a class graph to show the frequency of particular length flights – it will be easiest to do this by banding certain lengths. For example, one band might contain four teddies who flew between 3 and 3.5 metres.
National Curriculum: AT 1/3 (i, ii); AT 2/3 (x, xi); AT 5/4 (iii)

Name length survey The children can collect up their information and compare name lengths. They can produce a class graph containing all the information. How many are there of each length of name? What is the longest? What is the shortest?
National Curriculum: AT 1/3 (ii); AT 5/3 (iv)

Card cover-up Discuss with the children who won. What do they think were their chances of being right first time? Can they see that there is a one in five chance of turning over the right card? After that, do their chances improve?
National Curriculum: AT 1/3 (ii); AT 5/3 (v, vi)

Card selection Play this game again in class. Several children can play it together. Discuss what are sensible totals to choose and what are silly ones. Why are some totals easier to get than others? Write a total, for example 12, in the middle of a circle and write all the ways of getting to it with two, three or more cards all around it. Choose another total. Are there more or less ways of getting it?
National Curriculum: AT 1/3 (i, ii, iv); AT 2/3 (ii); AT 5/3 (v, vi)

Coin choice Discuss with the children what the chances are of pulling out a particular coin. Do they see that it depends on how many of that particular coin are included in the bag? If there are lots of pennies, and very few 50p coins, what are the relative chances of getting a 50p over a penny? How could the game be made fair to all coins? Would it make any difference if there was one of each or two of each?
National Curriculum: AT 1/3 (i, ii, iv); AT 5/3 (v, vi)

Circle choice Play this again in class. Several children can play it together. Discuss what are sensible numbers to put in their circles and what are silly ones. Why are some totals easier to get than others? Write a total, for example 12, in the middle of a circle and write all the ways of getting it by throwing the dice once, twice or three times around it. Choose another total. Are there more or less ways of getting it?
National Curriculum: AT 1/3 (ii); AT 2/3 (ii); AT 5/3 (v, vi, vii)

Dice multiplication The children can compare their games. How did they choose the numbers? Why are some totals easier to get than others? Write a number, for example 12, in the middle of a circle and write around it all the ways of getting it by throwing the dice twice and multiplying the totals. Choose another number. Are there more or less ways of getting it? Which are good numbers to have at the beginning of the track and at the end?
National Curriculum: AT 1/3 (i, ii, iii); AT 2/3 (iii); AT 5/3 (v, vii)

Probability quiz The children can give each other their quiz questions and compare their answers to those given here: 1 in 2 and 1 in 4. Can they justify their answers? You could make a class book of quiz questions.
National Curriculum: AT 1/3 (ii); AT 5/3 (v, vi, vii)

Predicting the chance The children can share their predictions with one another. Make either a display or a class book of their 'successful' predictions. Which set has more in it? Encourage them to give subjective justifications for their predictions.
National Curriculum: AT 1/3 (ii); AT 5/3 (v)

Alphabet choice The children can play this in class. How can they alter the number of letters in the bag and make it more likely that they will be able to make a word? Discuss the chances of getting a vowel. You could record 100 choices from the bag and see how many vowels are drawn out. (Remember to replace the letter each time.) This will give you a percentage. If the children do this several times the percentage should be a fairly accurate reflection of the chances.
National Curriculum: AT 1/3 (i, ii, iv); AT 5/3 (v, vi, vii)

Square the circle Discuss with the children who won. What do they think were their chances of being right first time? Can they see that there is more chance of turning over the right cards the second time? After that, how much do their chances improve? Encourage the children to give subjective justifications of their chances.
National Curriculum: AT 1/3 (ii); AT 5/3 (v, vi)

Race to 100 The children can play this again in class – it is very good for their mental arithmetic! What are the factors which increase the probability of their being able to do it? How much does luck play a part and how much is skill?
National Curriculum: AT 1/3 (ii); AT 2/3 (ii); AT 5/3 (v, vi)

Phone number count-up

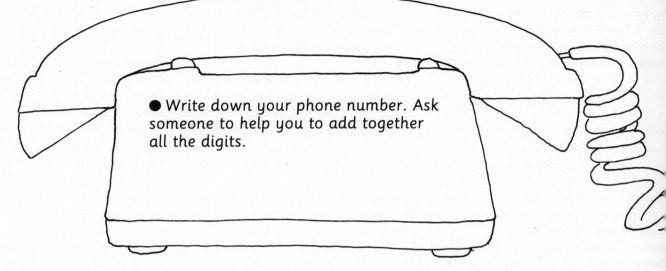

● Write down your phone number. Ask someone to help you to add together all the digits.

For example:

703536 ⇒ 7 + 0 = 7

7 + 3 = 10

10 + 5 = 15

15 + 3 = 18

18 + 6 = 24

● Keep adding until you reach a single digit.

For example:

24 ⇒ 2 + 4 = 6

This phone number reduces to 6.

● Collect as many phone numbers as you can. Find what they all reduce to.

● Can you find a phone number to reduce to each number from 1 to 9?

● Bring your lists into school.

impact MATHS HOMEWORK

Breakfast survey

● Who has what for breakfast?

● Conduct your own survey into breakfast-eating habits! Ask as many people as you can (including yourself!) what they regularly have for breakfast.

● Is it different at weekends? You may need to collect your data under two headings – one for weekdays and one for weekends.

● Design a chart on the back of this sheet to collect your data and bring it into school.

Dear Parent or Carer

We shall be using all the information the children collect to create a computer database and to decide how to represent what we find out graphically.

National Curriculum reference: AT 1 and AT 5

_____ and

child

_____

helper(s)

_____

did this activity together

_____and

child

_____

helper(s)

_____

did this activity together

Carbohydrate survey

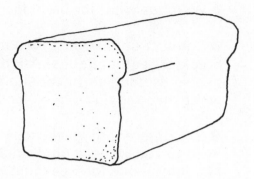

There are lots of different forms of carbohydrate (energy-giving, starchy foods) – potatoes, spaghetti, rice, bread and many others.

● Conduct a survey of the carbohydrates your family eats. What proportion of it is bread?

● Calculate how many meals you eat together in the week (for example, two on the weekdays and three on Saturday and Sunday) and work out the main carbohydrate in each meal. Then draw a small graph to represent your results.

Number counting

'How many nines are there?' This seems an odd question. Turn it around like this.

● A printer is printing a book with 1000 pages. He comes up and tells you that the number '9' has gone wrong on his printing machine. How many page numbers will be affected?

● Work with someone else to find out.

● Bring all your working into school.

_____and

child

_____

helper(s)

_____

did this activity together

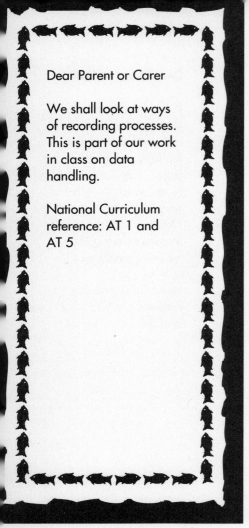

_____and

child

_____

helper(s)

_____

did this activity together

Phone book

How easy is it to access information in the phone book?

● Ask someone to help you to look up a friend's or relation's number.

● How do you do this? Draw a flow chart to indicate the process.

● Now try out your flow chart by looking up another number. Does it work? You may need to adapt it.

● Bring your flow chart into school.

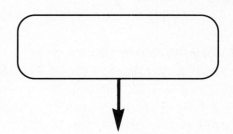

impact MATHS HOMEWOR

Five ways

● How many ways are there of making 5, using just addition? There is 2 + 3 and 1 + 1 + 1 + 1 + 1 and so on. But how many ways are there in all? And how can you prove that you have found them all?

● Work on this with someone in your house.

● Lay out your information in a methodical fashion. When you have sorted out 5, try 6.

● Bring your trials into school.

Dear Parent or Carer

We are looking at ways of recording our information in a systematic and logical fashion. This is part of our work on data handling.

National Curriculum reference: AT 1, AT 2 and AT 5

_____and

child

_____

helper(s)

_____

did this activity together

_____and

child

_____

helper(s)

_____

did this activity together

Favourite pastimes

● What are your favourite pastimes? What do you spend a great deal of your time doing? Perhaps you play with LEGO? Perhaps it is the computer or dolls' houses?

● Ask someone to help you make a list opposite in order of preference.

● Can you categorise the items on your list? Are some more active than others?

impact MATHS HOMEWORK

Electrical apparatus

● How many items of electrical apparatus could there be in a really up-to-date, mechanised home? Ask someone to help you to think of all the possible items of electrical apparatus which there could be in a home.

● Try to list all the items under different categories. What categories can you think of?

● Bring all your lists into school.

Dear Parent or Carer

We shall use all the information which the children collect to create categories and analyse and represent our data. This will involve a simple computer database.

National Curriculum reference: AT 1 and AT 5

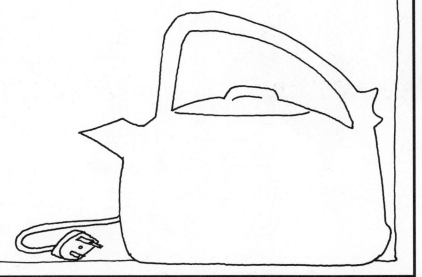

_____ and

child

_____

helper(s)

_____

did this activity together

Phone call survey

- How many phone calls do people in your house get? Who gets the most? Who gets the least?

- How many phone calls do you make a day? A week?

- Calculate the approximate number of calls made and received in a year.

- Bring your information into school.

Letter count-up

- How many letters does your household receive in a week? Are they all bills?

- Calculate the number of letters received at your address in a month and in a year.

- Categorise them under two headings – pleasant and unpleasant! How many (roughly) in each category?

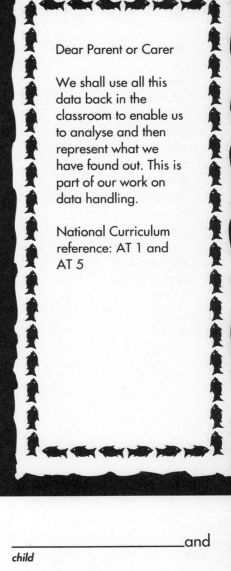

Dear Parent or Carer

We shall use all this data back in the classroom to enable us to analyse and then represent what we have found out. This is part of our work on data handling.

National Curriculum reference: AT 1 and AT 5

_____and

child

_____

helper(s)

_____

did this activity together

_____and

child

_____

helper(s)

_____

did this activity together

Subtraction survey

● What different methods do people use to do subtraction sums? Does it depend on the sum? Do they do some in their heads, some using paper and pencils and some on a calculator? Which methods do they use?

● Carry out your own survey. Use these sums:

$$20 - 4 =$$

$$43 - 18 =$$

$$10,000 - 1 =$$

$$85 - 34 =$$

● Devise a way of recording how people do these sums. Give them to as many people as you can. Note whether they use a calculator, paper and pencil (make sure these are available!) or if they do them in their heads.

● Which ones do people have trouble with?

● Do they all get them all right?

● Remember to do them yourself first so that you know what the answers are!

● Bring all your data into school.

"43-18=????"

Getting up!

● At what times do different people get up? Who gets up first in your house? Who gets up last? Is it different at weekends?

● Survey as many people – friends and relations – as you can! They do not have to give their names, but write down what time they get up – in the week and at weekends – and record their approximate ages, their genders and occupations.

● Design a chart to record all this information and bring it into school. You could use the back of this sheet.

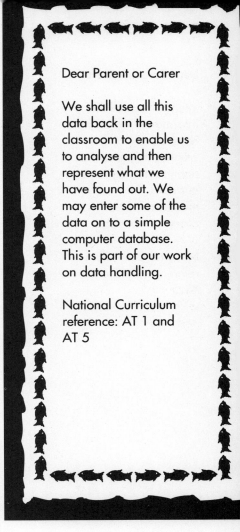

Dear Parent or Carer

We shall use all this data back in the classroom to enable us to analyse and then represent what we have found out. We may enter some of the data on to a simple computer database. This is part of our work on data handling.

National Curriculum reference: AT 1 and AT 5

_____and

child

_____

helper(s)

_____

did this activity together

_____and

child

_____

helper(s)

_____

did this activity together

Sweatshirt survey

● Do you wear sweatshirts? Does anyone else in your family wear them? We are doing a survey of sweatshirts.

● What type is the most popular? Should they have hoods, collars or plain round necklines? Should they have something on the front or be plain? Should they be one colour or more than one colour? What images on the front are good – names, pictures, brand names and so on.

● Survey as many people as you can, of all ages and design a chart to record all the information you collect.

● Bring your information back into class.

What do you read?

● What sorts of things do you like reading – books, adventure stories, romances, comics, magazines, the back of the cereal packet …?!

● Think of all the categories of reading matter that you can (don't forget newspapers!) and make a chart. Start below.

● Then ask as many people as you can find what they like reading best.

● Don't forget to include yourself!

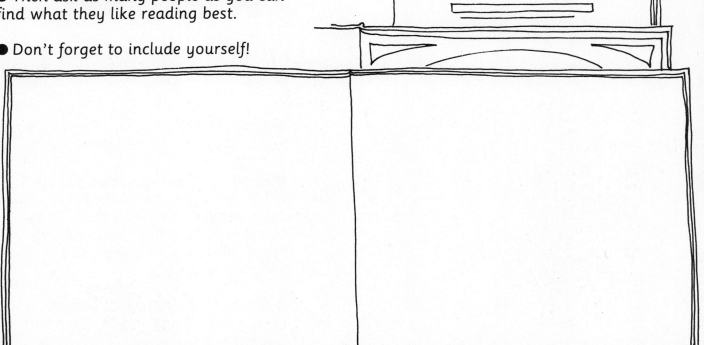

Dear Parent or Carer

We shall share all our information and then analyse and represent what we have learned graphically. This will assist us with our work on data handling.

National Curriculum reference: AT 1 and AT 5

_____and

child

_____

helper(s)

_____

did this activity together

_____and
child

_____
helper(s)

_____

did this activity together

Favourite sport

● What is your favourite sport? It could be one that you play or one that you really like to watch on TV.

● What sports do other people in your home like to watch or play?

● Conduct a survey asking people which are their favourite sports. Collect their answers and write them in the space opposite under two headings: those they enjoy playing and those they like to watch.

● Ask as many people as you can and bring all your information back into school.

impact MATHS HOMEWORK

Back-pack survey

● Do you or does anyone in your house own a backpack?

● If the answer is yes, what sort of backpack is it?

● If the answer is no, do you know anyone with a backpack? It could be a rucksack or a school bag.

● Find a backpack and draw it carefully on the back of this sheet. Choose some words to describe it – for example: large, small, square, oblong, oval, coloured, patterned, has a picture on it and so on.

● Bring all your information and your drawing into class.

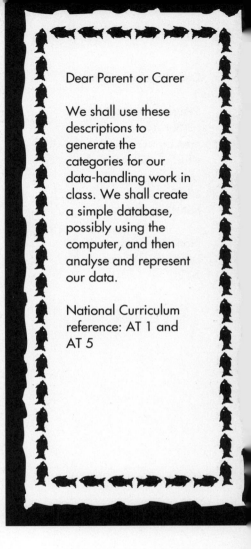

Dear Parent or Carer

We shall use these descriptions to generate the categories for our data-handling work in class. We shall create a simple database, possibly using the computer, and then analyse and represent our data.

National Curriculum reference: AT 1 and AT 5

_____and

child

_____

helper(s)

_____

did this activity together

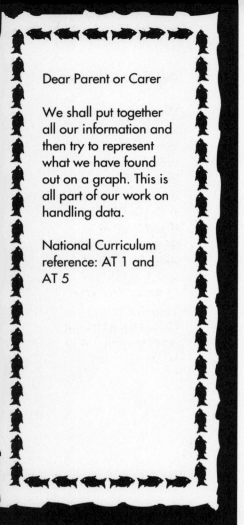

_____and

child

_____

helper(s)

_____

did this activity together

Fruit and vegetables

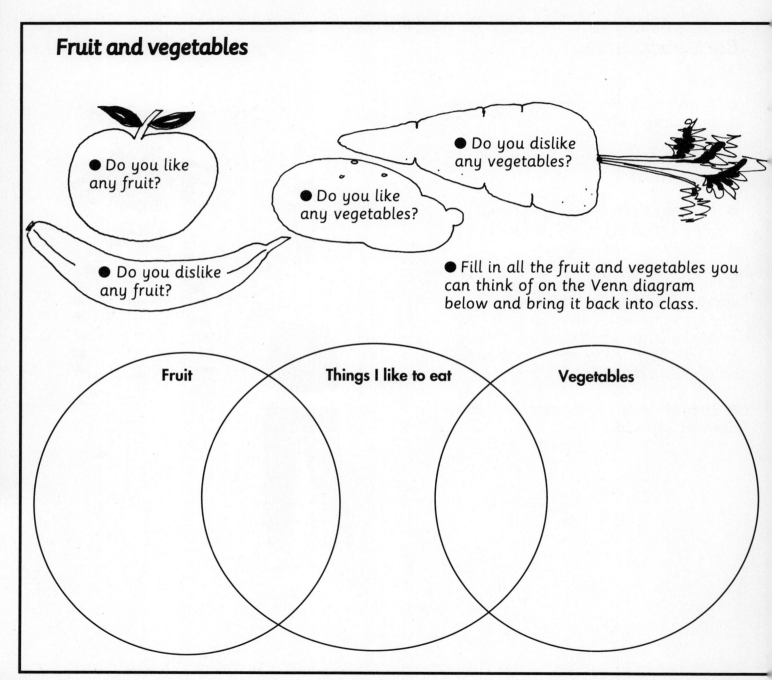

● Do you like any fruit?

● Do you dislike any fruit?

● Do you like any vegetables?

● Do you dislike any vegetables?

● Fill in all the fruit and vegetables you can think of on the Venn diagram below and bring it back into class.

Fruit   **Things I like to eat**   **Vegetables**

impact MATHS HOMEWORK

Cat survey

● There do seem to be a lot of cats around! We are going to carry out a cat survey.

● All weekend, keep your eyes peeled for cats.

● Record every cat you see – write down its colour and size. Start by using the space below.

● Devise a chart to collect your information.

● Bring all your findings into school. Have fun!

_____and

child

_____

helper(s)

_____

did this activity together

_____and

child

_____

helper(s)

_____

did this activity together

Teddy distance

How far can you throw your teddy?!

YOU WILL NEED: a piece of string exactly 1 metre long and a teddy who will not be hurt by being thrown!

● Ask someone to help you work out how far you can throw him. You may need to go outside to try. Measure the distance teddy 'flies' using your metre string.

● Record the distance. You may want to have more than one go, in which case you may bring several distances into class.

impact MATHS HOMEWORK

Name length survey

What is an average length of name?

● Write down your name – first name and surname – and count how many letters it is.

My name is :
_____

It has ☐ letters.

● Now do the same with as many people as you can this weekend. We want to see what is the average length of name.

● Write all your information opposite and bring it back into class.

Dear Parent or Carer

We shall put together all our information and analyse it in some detail. We may use a simple computer database to help us with this.

National Curriculum reference: AT 1 and AT 5

_____and

child

_____

helper(s)

_____

did this activity together

_____and

child

_____

helper(s)

_____

did this activity together

Card cover-up

YOU WILL NEED: ten cards numbered 1–10 (from a pack will do or make your own) and two 1p coins.

● Shuffle the cards and lay out five face down in front of each of you.

● Then each of you takes it in turns to shut their eyes or turn round while the other player hides a 1p coin underneath one of their cards.

● Take it in turns to guess which of your opponent's cards the coin is under.

● If you are wrong, score the value of the card turned over.

● If you are right, stop guessing and let your opponent go on guessing.

● Play five times – the person with the lowest score is the winner.

impact MATHS HOMEWORK

Card selection

Dear Parent or Carer

This activity is designed to help children think about mathematical probability and the chances of particular outcomes occurring. We shall be talking about how good – or poor – these chances are in class.

National Curriculum reference: AT 1, AT 2 and AT 5

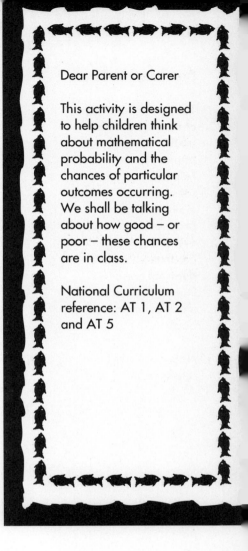

YOU WILL NEED: a pack of cards with the face (picture) cards removed.

● Shuffle the cards and place them in a pile face down. Take it in turns with your helper to lift a card from the pack. Before you start, you must each say a total above ten – for example, 'Twelve'.

● When you turn over your card, you keep it in your hand. The first person to

make the total they said, using some or all of the cards in their hand, is the winner and scores ten points.

● Play again and see who wins this time.

● The overall winner is the first person to get 30 points.

_____and

child

_____

helper(s)

_____

did this activity together

_____and

child

_____

helper(s)

_____

did this activity together

Coin choice

YOU WILL NEED: a large handful of change and a paper or cloth bag.

● Place all the coins in the bag.

● Take it in turns with someone to fish in the bag and choose a coin.

● Hold it in your hand so that it cannot be seen. The other person has to guess what coin it is.

● If they are correct, they keep the coin. If they are wrong, put it back into the bag. Now let them fish into the bag and you guess.

● Play until all the coins are gone from the bag.

● Who has the most money?

● Play again. Is it easier to guess the second time around?

impact MATHS HOMEWORK

Circle choice

YOU WILL NEED: a dice, a pencil, an eraser and the score cards below.

● Each of you should draw three circles on your piece of paper. Write in three numbers between 3 and 18 inclusively.

● Take it in turns to throw the dice. You may choose to throw it once, twice or three times. Add the numbers thrown. If you make one of the totals in your circles, cross it out.

● The first person to cross out all three circles is the winner.

● Play again. Think carefully about what will be good numbers to put in your three circles.

● Who wins this time?

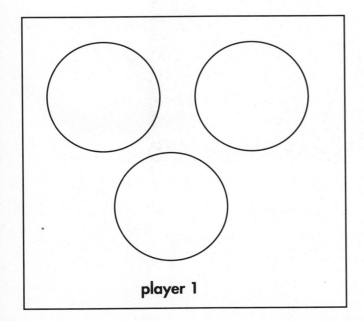

player 1

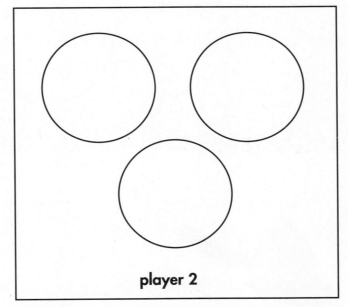

player 2

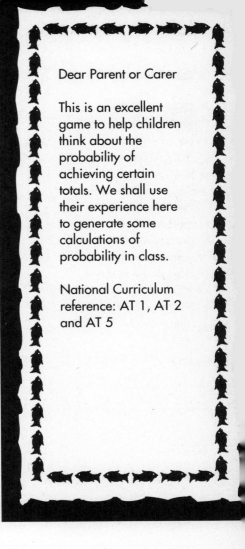

Dear Parent or Carer

This is an excellent game to help children think about the probability of achieving certain totals. We shall use their experience here to generate some calculations of probability in class.

National Curriculum reference: AT 1, AT 2 and AT 5

_____and

child

_____

helper(s)

_____

did this activity together

_____and

child

_____

helper(s)

_____

did this activity together

Dice multiplication

● You are going to design a multiplication game.

● The rules will be that you take it in turns to throw a dice twice and multiply together the numbers thrown. You may then move on to the next space showing that total.

● Bearing this in mind, fill in numbers all along the track which will make the game play well.

● Try out your track with someone at home and bring it into class.

Dice multiplication

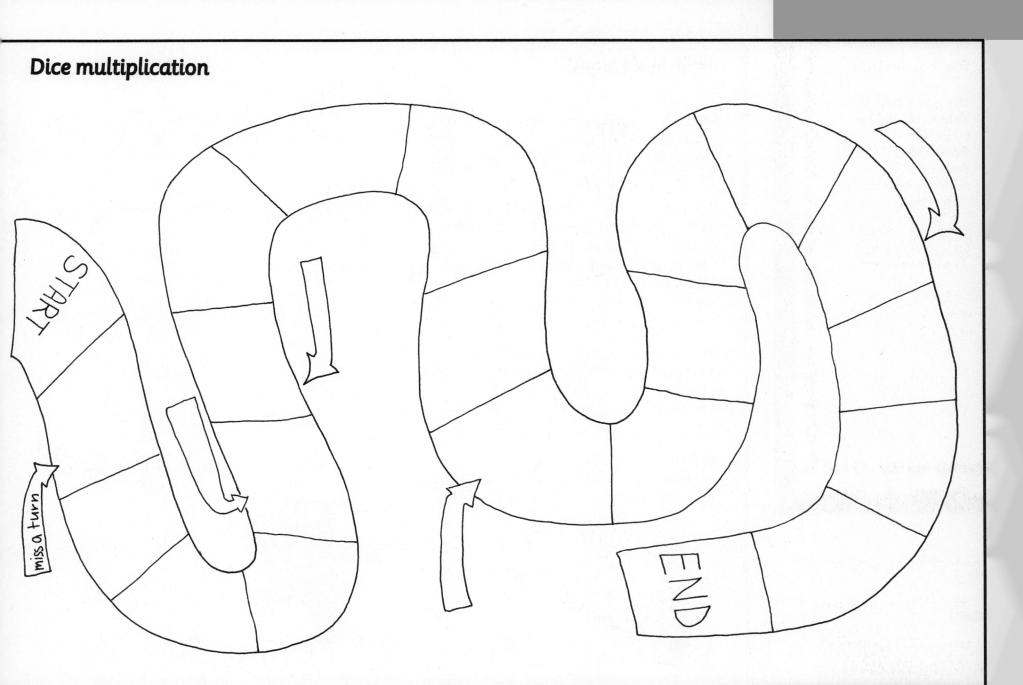

START

miss a turn

END

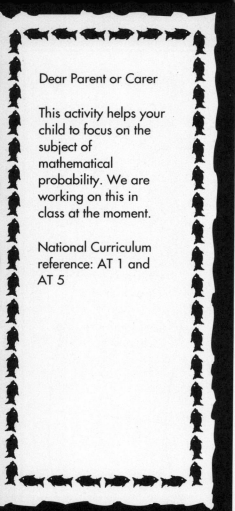
_____and

child

_____

helper(s)

_____

did this activity together

Probability quiz

● You are throwing a dice. If you have six throws, and someone bets you that you will NOT throw a 6, are you likely to win?

● You are tossing a coin. It lands heads, then it lands heads again. What are the chances of its landing heads on the next throw?

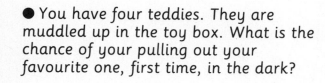

● You have four teddies. They are muddled up in the toy box. What is the chance of your pulling out your favourite one, first time, in the dark?

● Can you think of some more probability quiz questions? Bring them into class to try out on your friends.

Predicting the chance

● If someone asks you to name an event that you can be reasonably certain WILL happen in the next ten minutes, can you do so? (The chances must be good, but not certain!) Write down what it is.

```
[                    ]
```

● Wait ten minutes. Did it happen? Record whether your prediction was correct or not!

```
[                    ]
```

● Think of an event that you can be reasonably certain WILL NOT happen in the next ten minutes. Write this one down.

```
[                    ]
```

● Wait ten minutes. Did it happen? Record whether it did or not!

```
[                    ]
```

● Bring your predictions into school.

Dear Parent or Carer

Help your child to think of some amusing events, such as, 'Fred will wash his hands!' (likely), or 'The cat will catch that bird!' (unlikely). We are doing some work on the mathematical study of probability in class at the moment and this will feed into it.

National Curriculum reference: AT 1 and AT 5

_____and

child

_____

helper(s)

_____

did this activity together

_____and

child

_____

helper(s)

_____

did this activity together

Alphabet choice

YOU WILL NEED: a paper bag and 26 small pieces of paper.

● Cut out a series of pieces of paper and write the letters of the alphabet on them.

● Muddle them up in a paper bag.

● Shut your eyes and take three out. Can you make a word?

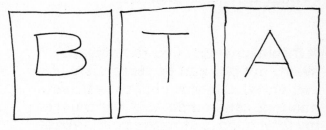

● If you can, score 3 points.

● If you can't, put them back and let someone else have a turn.

● Play until someone has 9 points.

Square the circle!

YOU WILL NEED: five cards like the ones opposite (cut from the back of an old Christmas or birthday card) with the following shapes drawn on them: a square, a circle, a triangle, an oblong and an oval.

● Lay the cards out face down.

● Ask someone to choose two. They are trying to get the circle and the square.

● If they are right, they get 10 points. (They must be right about both.) If not, turn them both back face down. Then they can guess again.

● If they are right this time, they get 8 points. If not, turn them both back face down. Then they can guess again. If they are right about both this time, they get 6 points. If not, turn them both back over and they guess again. This time they only score 4 points. Keep playing like this until they have guessed correctly.

● Now you let them lay out the cards and you have a go at guessing.

● Who scored the most points? Play several times. Who wins?

Dear Parent or Carer

This activity helps children to develop a sense of the probability of certain outcomes. How likely is it that they will guess right first time? We shall be discussing this in our work on mathematical probability in class.

National Curriculum reference: AT 1 and AT 5

_____and

child

_____

helper(s)

_____

did this activity together

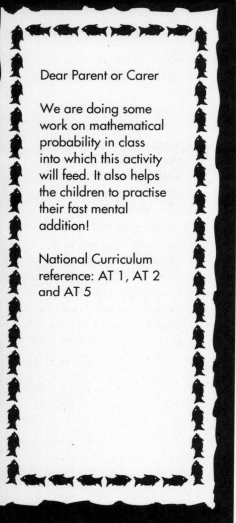
_____and

child

_____

helper(s)

_____

did this activity together

Race to 100

YOU WILL NEED: a dice.

● How likely is it that you can reach 100 by repeatedly throwing a dice and adding the numbers thrown within a time of five minutes?!

● Try doing this. Throw the dice as fast as you can, adding up the numbers as you go. Can you get to 100? How many times do you have to try in order to succeed?

impact MATHS HOMEWORK

Teachers' Notes
YEAR FIVE

Chapter count-up The children can collate all their information and arrange it on a graph to indicate the most frequent chapter lengths. This is easiest to do by banding chapters of similar length; 20–25 pages and so on. They can then see what is the most frequent chapter length (the mode). Perhaps they can calculate the average or mean too.
National Curriculum: AT 1/3 (i, ii); AT 2/3 (ii); AT 5/4 (v, vii)

Tapes galore Working in small groups the children could enter their information on to one database on the computer. They must agree the categories they are using. It is important that they realise that the choice of category is all important in establishing the database. They can then analyse their data and represent it on a class graph showing the frequency of different types of tape.
National Curriculum: AT 1/3 (ii); AT 5/3 (ii, iv)

Breathe now! The children can collate all their times on to a chart. They will need to band together certain times, for example 60–70 seconds, so that they can draw a graph showing the number of children who held their breath for a time within each band. Ten seconds may be a good band.
National Curriculum: AT 1/3 (ii); AT 2/4 (xvii); AT 5/4 (v)

Sleep survey The children can collate their information on a graph. They will need to decide how to group their data into suitable intervals, for example 55–60 hours per week. They can then produce a class graph. What is the average number of hours slept in a week – think about the mode (the most popular interval) and the mean (use a calculator to find this)?
National Curriculum: AT 1/4 (i, ii); AT 2/4 (xvii); AT 5/4 (v)

The technology of music The children can compare what they found out. Working in groups they can draw up a chart and then collate all of this information on to one large class graph. Talk about what you have discovered. How do they interpret this data? What does it tell us about current trends?
National Curriculum: AT 1/4 (i, ii); AT 5/3 (iv)

Mug survey Working in small groups the children could enter their information on to a database on the computer. They must agree the categories they are using. It is important in establishing the database. They can then analyse their data and represent it on a class graph showing the number of occurrences of different types of mug.
National Curriculum: AT 1/3 (ii); AT 5/4 (i, iii)

Days old! The children can collate their information on a graph. They will need to decide how to group their data into suitable intervals, such as 3700–3800 days. They can then produce a class graph.
National Curriculum: AT 1/4 (i, ii); AT 2/4 (xiv, xvii); AT 5/4 (v)

Plastic count-up Working in small groups the children could enter their information on to a computer database. They must agree the categories to use. How are they going to

group and classify all the plastic objects? They need to realise that the choice of category is all important in establishing the database. They can then analyse their data. They may then produce a graph or a chart.
National Curriculum: AT1/3 (ii); 5/4 (i, iii)

Bouncing balls The children can collate their information on to a graph. They will need to decide how to group their data into suitable intervals, such as 20–30 bounces. They can then produce a class graph. It will then be interesting to look at frequencies. Which numbers of bounces are the most frequently occurring? Can we talk about an average?
National Curriculum: AT 1/4 (i, ii); AT 5/4 (v)

High jump! First decide how the children are going to group their jumps in each band. Represent all their information on a class graph and look at the frequencies of different-sized jumps.
National Curriculum: AT 1/4 (i, ii); AT 2/4 (xvii); AT 5/4 (v)

Word check Working in groups the children can sort out how many of each lengths of word they have. Between the groups they can decide how many words there are – each group will have found some of which the others hadn't thought. They can then get together to combine all their information on a class graph. Look at the frequency of the different word lengths. Which is the most common? Which is the least common?
National Curriculum: AT 1/4 (ii); AT 5/4 (iii)

Word transformer The children can work together in groups and count up the number of four-step transformations, five-step transformations and so on. Let them look at each others'. Collect together the numbers for the whole class. Is there much variation? It

may not be appropriate to talk about the frequency of occurrence if they are all about the same length.
National Curriculum: AT 1/4 (ii); AT 5/4 (iii)

Toy sort The children can share their tree diagrams with one another and talk about the categories they used. Did they all choose the same? Were some different? Can they create a large tree diagram with lots of branches working together?
National Curriculum: AT 1/4 (i, ii); AT 5/4 (vi)

Comic survey Working in small groups, the children could enter their information on to a simple database on the computer. They must agree the categories they are using. How are they going to group and classify all the types of comics: those for girls/boys or humorous/ adventure/educational? It is important that they realise that the choice of category is all important in establishing the database. They can then analyse their data. They may then produce a graph or chart.
National Curriculum: AT 1/3 (ii); AT 5/4 (i, iii)

Six-a-minute The children can work in groups of five or six and collate all their data. How many sixes did they throw? What was the average of all their combined throws and how are they going to work it out? Discuss this. Discuss also other possible averages, for example the mode (most frequently occurring number) and the median (the middle value).
National Curriculum: AT 1/3 (ii); AT 5/4 (iii, iv)

Letter averages The children can work in small groups and collate their numbers. How many occurrences of 's' did they find over all? Now try and make a whole class graph showing the frequency. Discuss the average. Would they be better looking at the mode (most frequently occurring number)?

Suppose they were to try another letter. Which letter might be as common? Or more common?

National Curriculum: AT 1/3 (ii); AT 5/4 (iii, iv, v)

My favourite song Look at the categories the children and their parents have constructed. Did one person have a category that no one else had? Were some categories more frequent than others? Collate all your data on to a class graph. Discuss which of the categories you will use. What was the most frequently occurring type of song?

National Curriculum: AT 1/4 (i, ii); AT 5/4 (v)

Living relations Discuss which relation is the oldest in the whole class? Which is the youngest? Make a graph of all the relations in the whole class. Write the years – in groups (every five, or may be ten years) – along the bottom of the graph and the number of relations in that category above it.

Which is the most common category? Discuss what shape the graph makes? Can the children explain why?

National Curriculum: AT 1/4 (i, ii); AT 2/4 (xvi); AT 5/4 (iii, v)

What a chance Discuss why the chances of being right increase as the game goes on. Was anyone right first time? What are the chances of this happening? One in ten? Can they add some more cards and invent a harder game? Can they add more cards and keep the chances the same?

National Curriculum: AT 1/3 (ii); AT 5/4 (viii, ix)

Card sharp Discuss who guessed right. Did anyone guess right three times in a row? How likely is this – very likely, not at all likely, very unlikely? Play the game in class. Tell the children to write down the cards they pick up for an incorrect guess in their maths books. Is their addition correct? How can the children make the game easier?

National Curriculum: AT 1/3 (ii); AT 5/4 (viii)

Get to the top! The children can swap their variations on the basic game. Who thought up a really good one? Did any two people think up the same one? Discuss with the children how they decided that a total was 'hard' to get from adding two or three dice numbers, and how they decided that a total was 'easy' to get. List all the possible totals as a class.

National Curriculum: AT 1/4 (i, ii); AT 5/4 (viii, ix)

Heads or tails? Working in groups of five or six, the children can collate all

their findings. Make a list of all the possible outcomes. Which are the most and least likely? What are the chances of getting each one?

National Curriculum: AT 1/4 (i, ii); AT 5/4 (viii, ix, x)

Smarties choice Make a class graph of the numbers of different coloured Smarties you all found: colours along the bottom of the graph and total numbers up the side. Whose packet came nearest the class graph? That is, if red was overall most likely, in whose packet was red most likely? In terms of likelihood, did anyone's packet exactly mirror the graph?

National Curriculum: AT 1/4 (i, ii); AT 5/4 (viii, ix)

Evens! Make a class book of all the children's suggested events. Which ones go in the category of 'an even chance'?

Which go in the category of 'a better than even chance' and which go in the category of 'a worse than even chance'? Discuss how likely are some of the children's choices.

National Curriculum: AT 1/3 (ii); AT 5/3 (vi)

Wakey! Wakey! Collate your information on to a class graph. How many names are there above the '1 in 7' chance? What about the '1 in 2' chance? Make a long graph. Discuss who is very likely to wake up and who is not! Suppose someone wakes up on time everyday except Christmas Day, what can we say are their chances?

National Curriculum: AT 1/3 (i, ii); AT 5/4 (viii, ix)

Chapter count-up

● How long is the average chapter in your reading book. Ask someone to help you to find out.

● Study the book you are currently reading. Look at each chapter and write down its length below.

● If you can, do this for another book or two as well.

● Bring all your information into school.

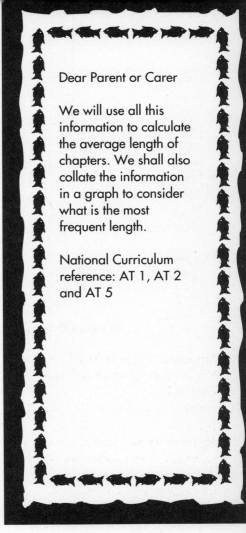

Dear Parent or Carer

We will use all this information to calculate the average length of chapters. We shall also collate the information in a graph to consider what is the most frequent length.

National Curriculum reference: AT 1, AT 2 and AT 5

_____and

child

_____

helper(s)

_____

did this activity together

_____and

child

_____

helper(s)

_____

did this activity together

Tapes galore

Do you have a cassette player? Do you play music or listen to stories? Do you borrow cassettes from the library?

● Make a tape survey of people in your house.

● Design a chart to collect your information. We want to know what type of tape each person listens to, what they prefer and how much they listen to their tapes.

For example; an older brother might prefer jazz and he might listen to his jazz tapes every evening – about four hours a day. You might prefer stories, and listen to those for an hour at bedtime.

Breathe now!

● How long can you hold your breath? Ask someone to help you time yourself not breathing!

● Ask as many people as you can to do the same thing! (Don't ask anyone for whom it might be dangerous – like someone who is very old or not well or a baby!)

● Set up a chart to record your information. Use the space below. Write their names and give a space for the number of seconds.

● Find a watch with a second hand or a means of timing seconds.

● Time as many people as you can.

● Who held their breath for the longest?

● Bring all your information into school.

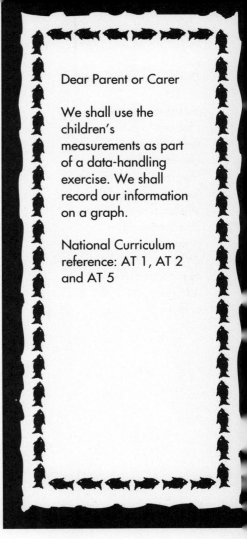

Dear Parent or Carer

We shall use the children's measurements as part of a data-handling exercise. We shall record our information on a graph.

National Curriculum reference: AT 1, AT 2 and AT 5

_____and

child

_____

helper(s)

_____

did this activity together

_____and

child

_____

helper(s)

_____

did this activity together

Sleep survey

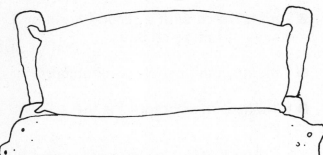

● How much do you sleep each week? How much do other people in your house sleep each week?

● Ask someone to help you calculate the number of hours each person sleeps in the week.

● How many hours do they sleep each day? Is it the same every day? If not, you will have to add up each day separately.

● Use the space opposite to start your working out.

● Bring all your information into school.

impact MATHS HOMEWORK

The technology of music

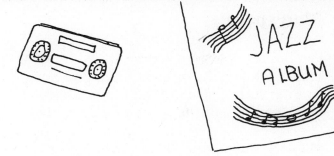

Some people say that cassettes and record players are not being made or used because of CDs. We shall do our own survey to find out.

● Ask as many people as you can if they have a CD player, a tape deck or cassette player or a record player. Some people may have all three! Some may not have any. Remember to remind people that they may have a cassette player in the car!

● Design your own chart to record all your information. It would be helpful if you can record the approximate age of each person being surveyed since this may prove of interest when we are analysing our data.

Dear Parent or Carer

We shall use all this information to set up a database on the computer and then to analyse what we have discovered. This is part of our work on data handling and representation.

National Curriculum reference: AT 1 and AT 5

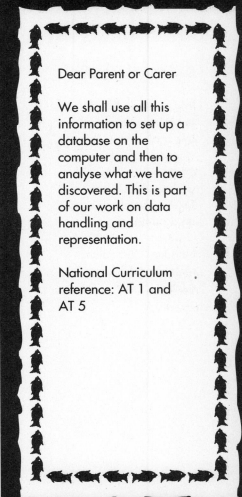

_____and

child

_____

helper(s)

_____

did this activity together

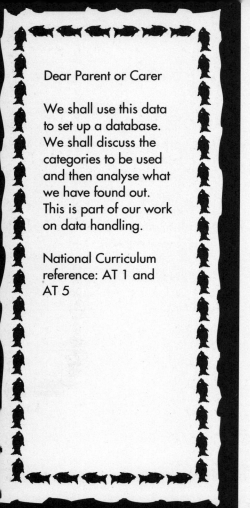

_____and

child

_____

helper(s)

_____

did this activity together

Mug survey

How many mugs or cups have you got
in your house? Have they got pictures
on? Are they all the same or different?

● Carry out a mug survey in your
home.

● How many mugs do you have?

We have

_____ mugs in our house.

● Classify them as best you can – cat
picture, flowers, plain blue and so on.
Write in the space opposite.

● Bring all your data back into school.

impact MATHS HOMEWORK

Days old!

● How many days old are you? Ask someone to help you work this out. You will need to use a calculator!

● Now find out how many days old the other members of your family are. Guess first! Write down your guess (based on the answer of how many days old you are).

● Bring your guesses and answers into school.

Dear Parent or Carer

We shall use all the information generated here in a data-handling exercise in class. We shall also be checking each other's arithmetic!

National Curriculum reference: AT 1, AT 2 and AT 5

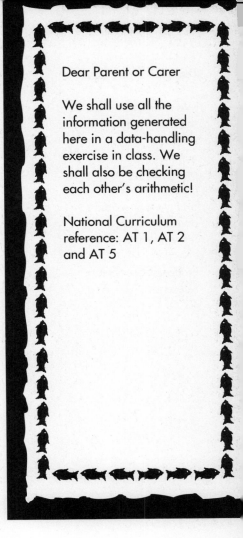

_____and

child

_____

helper(s)

_____

did this activity together

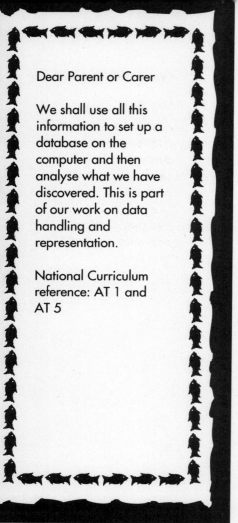

Dear Parent or Carer

We shall use all this information to set up a database on the computer and then analyse what we have discovered. This is part of our work on data handling and representation.

National Curriculum reference: AT 1 and AT 5

_____ and

child

_____

helper(s)

_____

did this activity together

Plastic count-up

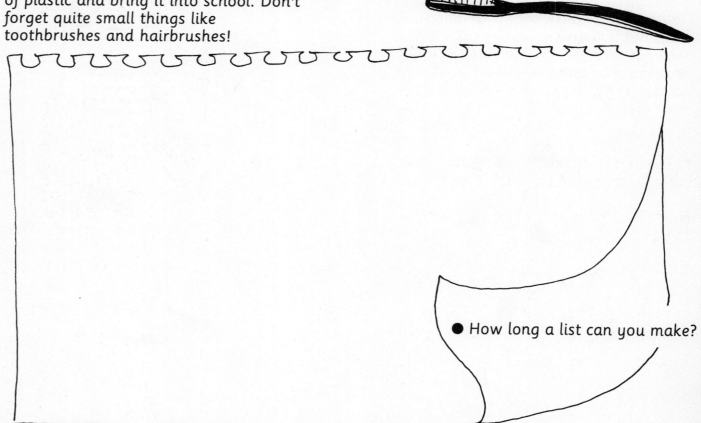

● How many things around you are principally made of plastic? Look around you and have a count up.

● Make a list below of all the things which you think are principally made of plastic and bring it into school. Don't forget quite small things like toothbrushes and hairbrushes!

● How long a list can you make?

impact MATHS HOMEWORK

Bouncing balls

How many times can you bounce a ball without stopping? Ask someone to help you find out.

YOU WILL NEED: a piece of paper (the back of this sheet will do), a pencil, a bouncy ball and somewhere safe to bounce it!

● First let your helper bounce the ball and you keep a tally of the number of bounces. Make a stroke for every bounce and a bar for every fifth like this: ⦀⦀⦀

● Then you bounce and they tally. You may want to practise first!

● Bring your records of bounces into school.

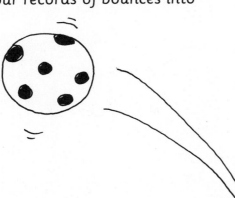

_____and

child

_____

helper(s)

_____

did this activity together

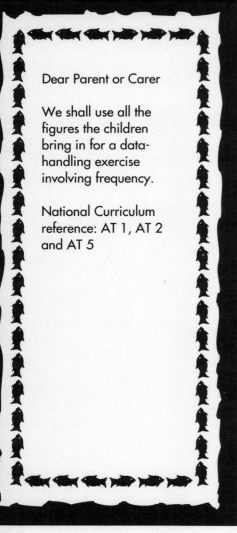
High jump!

How high can you jump? Ask someone to help you find out.

YOU WILL NEED: a rule or a tape measure and a place to jump safely!

● Basically, you jump and they measure! Ask your helper to hold the rule vertically and put a finger where you jumped up to. Then you both read off the distance.

● Measure how high someone else in your house can jump as well, if you like!

● Bring your measurements into school.

impact MATHS HOMEWORK

Word check

● Use the letters in the word 'mathematics' to make as many words as you can. Work on this over a period of time and involve as many members of your family as you can.

● When you have found as many words as you possibly can, arrange the

words in groups according to the number of letters. For example, put all the three-letter words together, put the four-letter words together and so on.

● Bring all your information into school.

mathematics

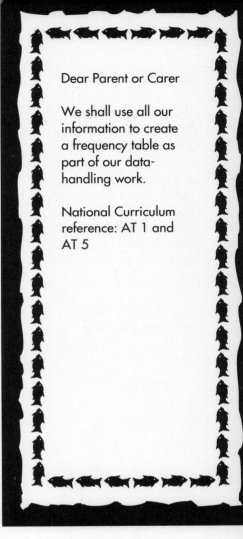

Dear Parent or Carer

We shall use all our information to create a frequency table as part of our data-handling work.

National Curriculum reference: AT 1 and AT 5

_____and

child

_____

helper(s)

_____

did this activity together

Word transformer

● Start with a four letter word. For example:　　　　CATS

● Change one letter each time:　　　MATS
　　　　　　　　　　　　　　　　　MATE
　　　　　　　　　　　　　　　　　MALE

until you have changed every letter in the original word:　　MILE

This one was very short – it took four steps to get from CATS to MILE.

Sometimes they take longer:　DOGS
　　　　　　　　　　　　　　BOGS
　　　　　　　　　　　　　　BAGS
　　　　　　　　　　　　　　BATS
　　　　　　　　　　　　　　BETS
　　　　　　　　　　　　　　BEES
　　　　　　　　　　　　　　BEEN

This one took six steps.

● Create some word transformations of your own. Each step must be a real word. How long or short are yours? Bring them all into school.

Toy sort

Are you ever told off because your toys are in a mess?!

● Create a tree diagram to sort your toys!

● Decide on the categories – for example:

• soft toy/hard toy;
• construction toy/not construction toy;
• needs batteries/doesn't need batteries.

● Bring your tree diagram into school.

Dear Parent or Carer

This activity is part of the children's work in statistics and data handling.

National Curriculum reference: AT 1 and AT 5

_____and

child

_____

helper(s)

_____

did this activity together

_____and

child

_____

helper(s)

_____

did this activity together

Comic survey

COMIC

● How many comics are there for sale in your local newsagent? What do they cost? Which one(s), if any, do you get?

● This weekend, ask someone if you can visit a newsagent and look at the comics. Make a list of what there is for sale for people of your age with their prices.

NOW ONLY

10p

● How can you categorise them all? Suggest below some categories in which they could be grouped.

● Do you think there is a reasonable selection?

● Bring your lists into school.

impact MATHS HOMEWORK

Six-a-minute

What is the average number of sixes you can throw in a minute using an ordinary dice?

YOU WILL NEED: a dice, a stop-watch and a piece of paper.

● Take it in turns with someone to throw the dice as fast as you can, noting down every six you get (just put a tally-mark on the paper). The person not throwing the dice does the timing – exactly one minute. Have at least six turns each.

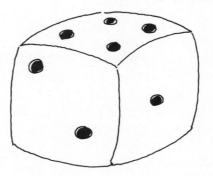

● What was the average number of sixes? (Add up the total number thrown and divide by the number of turns.)

Tally here:

Work out the average here:

● Bring all your working into school.

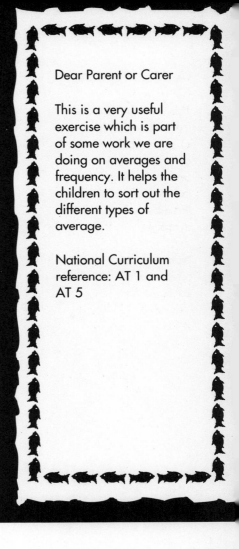

_____and

child

_____

helper(s)

_____

did this activity together

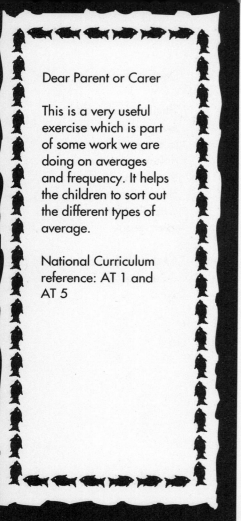
_____and

child

_____

helper(s)

_____

did this activity together

Letter averages

● What is the average number of times the letter 'S' is used in a line of print?

● Find a book and count out ten lines of print. Ask someone to help you to count the number of occurrences of 'S'. This is hard to do accurately, so be careful.

● Write down the number of 'S's below.

● Divide by ten.
● Write down your new answer.

● This is the average occurrence per line.

● Choose another ten lines. Do you get the same average? Write it below.

● Try another letter.

● Bring all your work into school.

My favourite song

● What is your favourite song?

● Conduct a survey to find out what is the favourite song of everyone you know.

● You must classify their answers. Are the songs 'Rock and Roll', 'Motown', 'Blues', 'Pop' or whatever?

● Bring your list of their answers, suitably classified, back into class.

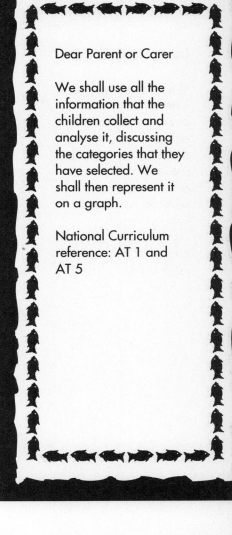

Dear Parent or Carer

We shall use all the information that the children collect and analyse it, discussing the categories that they have selected. We shall then represent it on a graph.

National Curriculum reference: AT 1 and AT 5

_____and

child

_____

helper(s)

_____

did this activity together

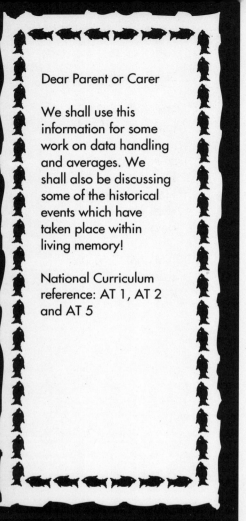

_____and

child

_____

helper(s)

_____

did this activity together

Living relations

● How old is your oldest living relation?

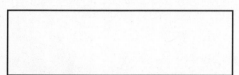

● How old is your youngest living relation?

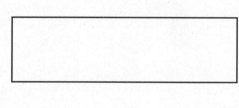

● Calculate the years in which they were each born.

● Bring all your information back into class.

What a chance

YOU WILL NEED: ten cards (cut out from an old cereal packet or the backs of old Christmas or birthday cards) numbered 1–10, a pencil and paper each!

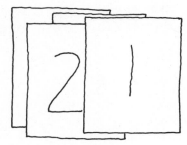

● Place the cards face down in a line.

● Take it in turns with your helper to turn one over. Before you do so, you must say what number you think it will turn out to be. If you are right, score 10 points. If you are wrong, leave it face up and let the other person have a turn. They should choose another card and guess what number it is going to be. If they are right, they score 9 points. If not, they leave the second card face up and let you have another turn.

● Keep playing like this. The number of points scored for a correct guess DECREASES as the number of the cards face up INCREASES.

● The winner is the person with the most points at the end.

● Play two or three times. Write down your scores on the back of this sheet.

● Write a sentence below explaining why you should score less as more cards are face up.

● Bring your scores and your sentence into school.

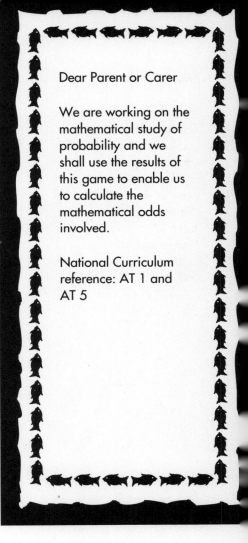

Dear Parent or Carer

We are working on the mathematical study of probability and we shall use the results of this game to enable us to calculate the mathematical odds involved.

National Curriculum reference: AT 1 and AT 5

_____and

child

_____

helper(s)

_____

did this activity together

_____and

child

_____

helper(s)

_____

did this activity together

Card sharp

YOU WILL NEED: a pack of cards with the face (picture) cards removed.

● Deal out three cards each to yourself and your helper. Leave the rest of the cards in a pile face down between you.

● Each of you is trying to guess the cards your opponent is holding. Take it in turns to guess a number, for example, 'Three'.

● If the guess is correct, the person holding the card must lay it face up in front them. If your guess is incorrect, you take a card off the pile and lay it beside you.

● Keep guessing each other's cards and taking a card from the pile for each incorrect guess. When all the cards being held are face up, count up the number of cards in the pile beside you. The person with the lowest number wins.

Get to the top!

YOU WILL NEED: a dice, a pencil and paper.

● Take it in turns with someone to throw the dice. You may throw it once, twice or three times. You are trying to get a score of 6 or 12 by adding the numbers thrown.

● If you get a total of 6, score 5 points. If you get a total of 12, score 10 points.

● Play until one of you has a score of 25 or over.

● Play a couple of times.

● Would it make a better game if you lost some points as well as gaining them? What totals on the dice could cause you to lose points? Remember they should not be totals which you get very often by throwing two or three dice.

● Try out any ideas you have.

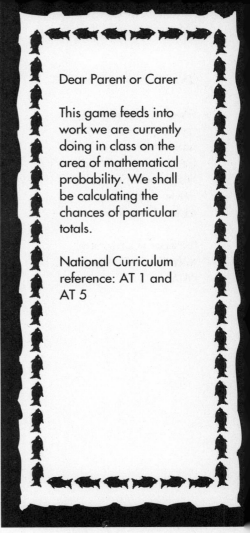

Dear Parent or Carer

This game feeds into work we are currently doing in class on the area of mathematical probability. We shall be calculating the chances of particular totals.

National Curriculum reference: AT 1 and AT 5

_____and

child

_____

helper(s)

_____

did this activity together

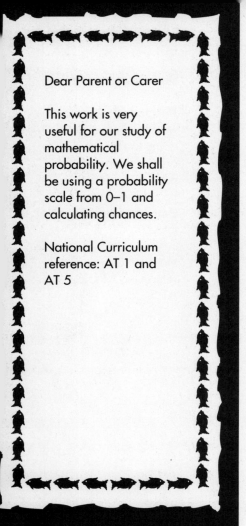
_____and

child

_____

helper(s)

_____

did this activity together

Heads or tails?

YOU WILL NEED: a handful (eight to ten) coins, a pencil and paper.

● Throw the coins in the air.

● How do they land? How many heads? How many tails?

● Repeat this several times. Record what you get.

● Now make a list below of all the possible ways the coins could ACTUALLY land, such as: H H H T T T T T

● Are you certain you have listed all the possible ways?

● Can you demonstrate that you have?

● Which ways are most likely? Which ways are least likely?

● Throw the coins in the air a few more times and see if your predictions seem to be correct.

● Bring your lists and results into school.

Smarties choice

YOU WILL NEED: a packet of Smarties, a plate, a paper bag, a pencil and paper (the back of this sheet will do).

● Tip out all the Smarties on to a clean plate.

● Count them and sort them into piles according to colour. Record how many there are of each colour.

● Put them all into a paper bag. Take it in turns with a helper to shut your eyes and take one out. Before you open your eyes, predict what colour it will be.

● Do this three or four times. How many times were you right?

● On your paper, write down which colour(s) the Smartie is MOST likely to be. Can you work out how likely this is?

● Write down the colour it is LEAST likely to be. Can you work out how likely this is?

● Bring all your figures into school.

Dear Parent or Carer

We are working on the study of probability and will be calculating the mathematical chances of certain outcomes.

National Curriculum reference: AT 1 and AT 5

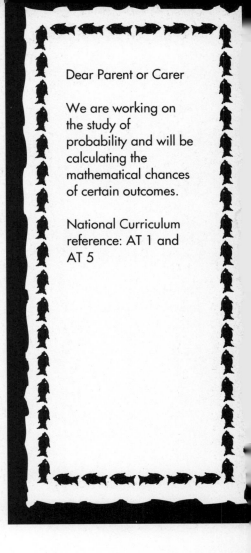

_____and

child

_____

helper(s)

_____

did this activity together

_____and

child

_____

helper(s)

_____

did this activity together

Evens!

● Can you think of two or three things which may happen over the next few days where the chance of their occurring is one in two (evens)?

● Write or draw them in the space below.

● Can you think of something where the chance of its happening is about one in twenty or thirty?

● Can you think of something where the chance of its happening is better than one in two?

● Write both of these things down too. Bring your answers into school.

Wakey! Wakey!

● What are the chances of you waking up on time?

● What are the chances of other people in your home waking up on time?

● Calculate the chances for each person by working out how many times a week (or a month if they are very bad at it!) they wake up on time and work out the odds (for example, one day in seven).

● Bring your calculations into school.

Dear Parent or Carer

We are working on the study of probability and will be giving and justifying subjective estimates of the mathematical chances of certain outcomes.

National Curriculum reference: AT 1 and AT 5

_____and

child

_____

helper(s)

_____

did this activity together

Teachers' Notes
Y E A R   S I X

Minutes old! Discuss how good various people's estimates were. Then collate all the ages in minutes on to a class graph. Discuss the class intervals – what will be the range of minutes in each category? Which category has the most people in it?
National Curriculum: AT 1/3 (i, ii); AT 2/4 (xvi); AT 5/4 (iii, v)

Initial letter list How many words did most people manage to write? Were some letters easier than others? Make a class graph with the letters along the bottom of the page and the numbers of words people managed to find above them. Which letters were hardest? You could also make a graph to show the different numbers of words individuals managed to find.
National Curriculum: AT 1/3 (i, ii); AT 5/3 (iv, v)

How many in a car? Draw up a large and brightly coloured class chart showing the different numbers of occupants people saw in cars. The children can then transfer this information on to a pie chart. Discuss the various sizes of the slices. Which number of occupants is most common? Which number is least common?
National Curriculum: AT 1/3 (i, ii); AT 5/4 (iii, v)

What do you want to know? Discuss the children's different surveys? Did any two children survey the same thing? Which surveys involved only a few people? How many people do the children feel they would have to poll in order to get a representative sample? Does it make a difference what you are trying to find out? Talk about representative samples. For example, should all the people asked be the same 'sort' of person?
National Curriculum: AT 1/4 (i, ii); AT 5/4 (iii, v)

Toasty timing This activity fits in very well with work on electricity and magnetism. The children can find out how much electricity it takes to cook a slice of toast. How much does this cost? Let the children look at an electricity bill and estimate how much electricity it takes to cook a slice of toast. How much do we spend a year on making slices of toast?! Time toasting a slice in class and do it accurately! Who agreed with the timing? Why might other people's figures have been different?
National Curriculum: AT 1/4 (i, ii); AT 5/4 (iii)

Money changing Ask the children to compare their different graphs. Make a class book or – better still – a display around a map showing all the different countries. How many of the countries visited use a decimal system of money (ten somethings to the next unit up)? Discuss why this might be popular.
National Curriculum: AT 1/4 (i, ii); AT 5/4 (iii, v)

Magazine content Discuss the categories the children chose. Did they all use the same? Were some categories appropriate for all types of magazine? Which ones were these?

Which categories were magazine-specific? Make some graphs for different types of magazine, for example women's magazines, computer magazines and so on. The children can work in groups and collate their data.
National Curriculum: AT 1/4 (i, ii); AT 5/4 (iii, v)

Eating times! Discuss how good various people's estimates were. Then collate all the times in hours on to a class graph. Discuss the class intervals – what will be the range of hours in each category? Which category has the most people in it? Discuss how we may interpret this data. Are those with the longest eating times necessarily the greediest? If not, why not? Consider the age of person (!), how slow or fast they eat and so on.
National Curriculum: AT 1/3 (i, ii); AT 2/4 (xvi); AT 5/4 (iii, v)

Slice of bread Discuss the different amounts that people calculated a slice to cost. Can you make a large class graph – discuss the price intervals (1–3p per slice and so on)? Put the prices, suitably grouped, along the bottom of the graph and the number of slices in each category up the side. Discuss how to interpret this data. Can we say that the lowest price per slice means the best value? If not, why not?
National Curriculum: AT 1/4 (i, ii); AT 5/4 (iii, v)

Tea bag tester Discuss how many cups of tea people managed to make! Draw up a class graph with the numbers of cups plotted against the number of children managing to make that number of cups; for example five children made 10 cups of tea with their tea bag. What was the average number of cups? Calculate this using the mode (most frequent),

the median (the middle value) and the mean (add them all up and divide by the total number). Which method of finding the average gives the fairest representation of data?
National Curriculum: AT 1/4 (i, ii); AT 5/4 (iii, iv, v, vii)

Growth rate! Discuss how many centimetres different children calculated that they grew each year. Did the children grow evenly or did they grow more in some years than others? Draw up individual graphs – which the children can work on in pairs, sharing each other's data – with each year plotted against the number of centimetres grown. Ask each child to work out what was the average number of centimetres that they grew? They can calculate this in three ways – using the mode (most frequent), the median (the middle value) and the mean (add them all up and divide by the total number). Which method of finding the average gives the fairest representation of their data?
National Curriculum: AT 1/4 (i, ii); AT 2/4 (xvi); AT 5/4 (iii, iv, v, vii)

Small shop or supermarket? Discuss where most people shop. How can the children represent all the data collected by the whole class? Given that there are only two categories – shop and supermarket – but different numbers of people doing a variety of amounts of shopping in each, how can this be most simply conveyed using a graph or pie chart? (Hint: they could produce two graphs or two pie-charts, each showing the various numbers of people who do 0–10% of their shopping there, 10–20% and so on. They can then compare the graphs/pie charts.) There are other ways!
National Curriculum: AT 1/4 (i, ii); AT 5/4 (iii, v)

Potato peeling The children can compare their varying times. Who was the quickest? Why do they think this was? Working in groups of five or six, they can choose the class intervals for the times: 0–60 seconds, 61–120 seconds and so on. What was the average time? Discuss different ways of finding the average: the median (the middle value), the mode (the most frequent) and the mean.
National Curriculum: AT 1/4 (i, ii); AT 5/4 (iii, iv, v, vii)

Essential items Make a large, brightly coloured chart based on a grid. You will need a list of all the items mentioned in the children's data down the side of the grid, and the words 'First, Second, Third...' along the top of the grid. Working as a class, read out the name of the first item, for example telephone. Ask the children to put up their hands if they saw it first. Suppose six hands go up. Write '6' in the 'First' column. Ask how many put it second. Suppose three put their hands up. Write '3' in the 'Second' column. Keep going like this. Now look at your chart. What do you notice? Are there clusters of high numbers? What does this tell us (for example, lots of people put the washing machine as essential, very few put the microwave!).
National Curriculum: AT 1/4 (i, ii); AT 5/4 (iii)

Card search Discuss what categories the children have suggested. Did all the children suggest the same ones? Were any categories found by only one or two children? Discuss the categories they should use for a class graph of all the numbers of different types of cards. Make a huge graph and let them take

it in turns to fill in the data. What was the most frequently occurring type of card? Why do they think this might be?
National Curriculum: AT 1/4 (i, ii); AT 5/4 (iii, v)

Birth pangs! Working in groups of five or six children, they can collate their data on to one graph. They will have to discuss what are reasonable class intervals to choose; for example, 2.00–4.00 am! Explain why the intervals should be the same. Compare the group graphs. Display them where all the children can see them. What can we learn? At what times are most babies born?
National Curriculum: AT 1/4 (i, ii); AT 5/4 (iii, v)

Pascal's probability Draw out a huge Pascal's Triangle and display it so that all the children can see. Discuss what each row means, and how we find out the number of possible outcomes (by adding each row). As a class, test it out for accuracy. Some people can take the first row, and do lots of trials. Others can take the second row, and so on. In this way, we can see if the reality matches the theory! Discuss the children's findings.
National Curriculum: AT 1/4 (i, ii, iii, iv); AT 5/4 (viii, ix, x)

How likely is rain? Discuss the children's estimates. Is there a reasonable degree of concurrence? Can they justify their estimate of the probability? Discuss what it means to say there is a 1 in 3 chance of it raining tomorrow. What would a 100% chance be? What would the chances be if we were in the middle of the Sahara? What about Africa in the rainy season?
National Curriculum: AT 1/4 (ii); AT 5/4 (vii, ix)

Cat chances Discuss how many throws each of the children had to have to collect a whole cat. If necessary, play the game in class again, in pairs, and ask the children to record the number of throws they had. Now make a class chart to show the number of throws; that is plot the number of throws against the number of children who got them. What is the average number of throws? Discuss the best sort of average in this context. Is it the mean or the mode?
National Curriculum: AT 1/4 (i, ii); AT 5/4 (iii, iv, v, vii)

Throw him down the stairs! Discuss the chances of each child being right. Did it make a difference how many stairs there were? Ask each child to work out the probability of teddy landing on that particular stair. (They may have to find out how many stairs there were if they forgot!) Is teddy equally likely to land on any stair?
National Curriculum: AT 1/4 (i, ii); AT 5/4 (viii, ix)

Five colours Working in pairs or small groups, the children can work out the actual chances of turning up each colour. For example, they have a 2 in 8 chance of turning up a green. This is the same as a 1 in 4 chance. Can they now play the game several times in pairs and record all their predictions and actual turns? Does the reality – what actually happened – match the theory?
National Curriculum: AT 1/4 (iii, iv); AT 5/4 (viii, ix)

Roll a letter The children can work in pairs or threes and calculate the odds of the penny landing on any one letter. How many 'E's are there on the grid? How many squares on the grid in all? What are the chances of

getting an 'E'? However, this assumes that all squares on the grid are equally likely to be landed on by the penny. Do the children think that this is the case? If not, why not? Which squares do they feel are more likely?
National Curriculum: AT 1/4 (iii, iv); AT 5/4 (viii, ix)

Coin or dice? The children can explain why they found the scoring system to be fair. What are the odds of being right in predicting the way the coin and the dice land? Can the children invent a game involving two coins and two dice? They will need to write down all the possible outcomes!
National Curriculum: AT 1/4 (i, ii); AT 5/4 (viii, ix, x)

Card divides Can the children explain why they think the scoring system is 'OK'? What are the chances of the 6 being the single card? What are the chances of its being in the first pile? Working in small groups, can they try out these possibilities? Are these fair? Perhaps they can invent some more in class?
National Curriculum: AT 1/4 (i, ii); AT 5/4 (viii, ix)

Probability puzzles Share all the answers the children got for these puzzles. Did they agree? They can try out all those they have brought in. Which ones are best? Are any impossible?! Make a class book of probability puzzles into which the children can dip and to which they – or you! – can add.
National Curriculum: AT 1/4 (i, ii); AT 5/4 (viii, ix, x)

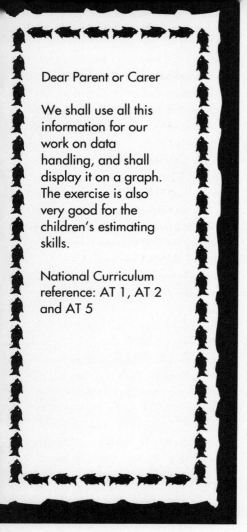

_____and

child

_____

helper(s)

_____

did this activity together

Minutes old!

● How many minutes old are you?

I am

minutes old

● Use your calculator to calculate how many minutes old everyone in your house is!

● Before you start this task, ask everyone to guess how many minutes old they are.

● Write down their guesses and your exact answers! Who was the closest?

Family member	Minutes old	
	Guess	Real age

Initial letter list

YOU WILL NEED: as many people as you can find to do this with you, a minute timer and a piece of paper and a pencil for each player.

● Everyone picks a letter and then somebody says, 'Go!' and starts the minute timer.

● Everyone starts writing down words beginning with their letter.

● When the one minute is up, count the number of words you have each written.

● Try again, each using a different letter. How many words did you write this time?

● Try one more time. Are you improving?

● Bring all your lists into school.

Dear Parent or Carer

We are going to use all this data to calculate different types of average using graphical representations of our data.

National Curriculum reference: AT 1 and AT 5

_____and

child

_____

helper(s)

_____

did this activity together

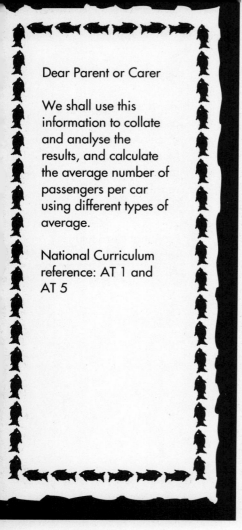

Dear Parent or Carer

We shall use this information to collate and analyse the results, and calculate the average number of passengers per car using different types of average.

National Curriculum reference: AT 1 and AT 5

_____and

child

_____

helper(s)

_____

did this activity together

How many in a car?

YOU WILL NEED: a pencil and a safe place from which to survey traffic passing.

● How many people are there in the average car? Watch the cars passing and record the number of occupants per car. You will need to draw up a chart in advance. Use the space below.

● With someone's help, collect as much data as you can. Note the time and day of your survey and where it was carried out.

● Bring your record sheet into class.

What do you want to know?

- Ask someone at home to help you to create your own survey!

- Decide what you intend to find out, and design a chart or tally sheet below to accumulate your data.

- Can you represent what you have discovered on a graph or chart?

- Bring all your work into school.

Dear Parent or Carer

We shall compare our surveys in class and discuss the different ways of collecting, analysing and representing our data.

National Curriculum reference: AT 1 and AT 5

_____and

child

_____

helper(s)

_____

did this activity together

_____and

child

_____

helper(s)

_____

did this activity together

Toasty timing

How long does it take to make a piece of toast?

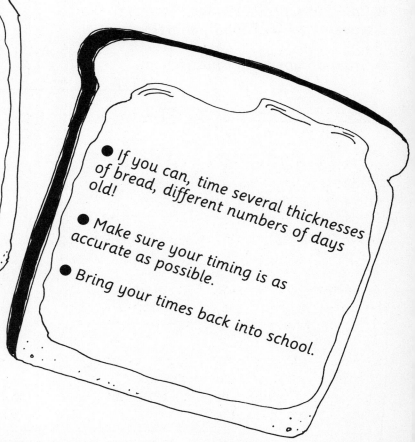

● Make several timings of toasting a slice of bread – start timing when the bread is put into the toaster or under the grill, and finish timing when it is done.

● Does the timing depend on how thick the bread is? Or how fresh?

● If you can, time several thicknesses of bread, different numbers of days old!

● Make sure your timing is as accurate as possible.

● Bring your times back into school.

impact MATHS HOMEWORK

Money changing

● Have you, or has anyone in your house, been abroad recently?

● What was the currency where they went and what is the rate of exchange? (You can look in a bank window or a newspaper for these.)

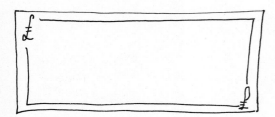

● Complete the conversion graph to enable you to convert British pounds into the currency of that country. Pounds are along the bottom, put the other currency up the side, and plot all the points you can.

For example, if I visited France, it might be 8 francs to the pound, so I can plot (1, 8) on my graph, and so on.

● What 'rule of thumb' did you or your friends or relations use to do quick conversions while they were abroad? How accurate was it?

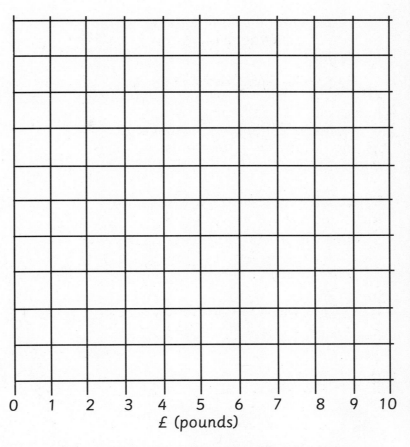

£ (pounds)

For example, in France I might think that 10 francs is about £1, then I could divide each number of francs by 10: 47f is about £4.70 and so on.

● Bring your conversion graphs into school.

Dear Parent or Carer

We shall be drawing conversion graphs in school and comparing their accuracy.

National Curriculum reference: AT 1 and AT 5

_____and

child

_____

helper(s)

_____

did this activity together

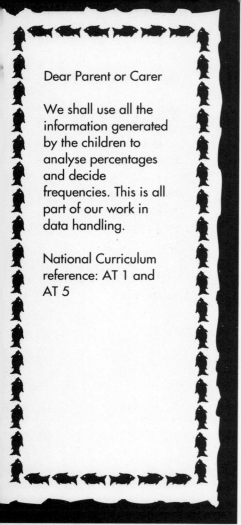

_____and

child

_____

helper(s)

did this activity together

Magazine content

What percentage of a magazine is adverts? Does it depend on the magazine?

YOU WILL NEED: an old copy of a magazine. (It can be any sort of magazine: a computer magazine, a fishing magazine, a woman's magazine....)

● Analyse and record the content of the magazine.

● First check how many pages there are:

Pages

● Then check the content – how does it divide? Think of appropriate categories, such as: 'stories', 'letter pages' or 'articles about specific items', 'readers' questions', 'what's new' and so on, as well as pages of adverts. List the number of pages in each category.

● Bring all your information back into school.

CAT WEEKLY

Eating times!

● How long each week do we spend eating? How many hours per year is this?

● Working with another person in your family, decide how long, on average, you each spend each day eating. You may have to calculate the weekdays and the weekends separately. Then calculate how many hours this is in a year!

● Do this for as many people in your family as you can. Bring all your data back into school.

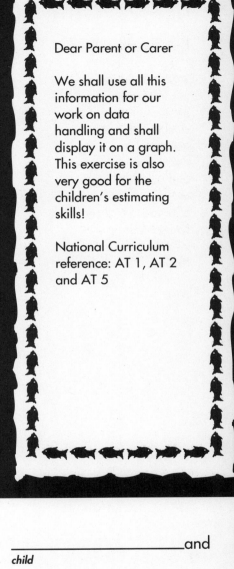

Dear Parent or Carer

We shall use all this information for our work on data handling and shall display it on a graph. This exercise is also very good for the children's estimating skills!

National Curriculum reference: AT 1, AT 2 and AT 5

_____and

child

_____

helper(s)

_____

did this activity together

Slice of bread

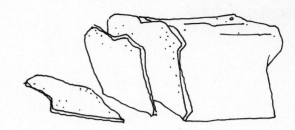

How much do we pay for each slice of
bread? We are going to check out the
value of different loaves.

● You will need to monitor how many
slices there are in your family loaf of
bread. If the bread is sliced, this simply
means counting, but if it is not, you
will have to set up a tally chart so that
every time someone in your house cuts
a slice of bread they remember to tick it
off on the chart! (HINT: put the tally
chart right by the bread bin!)

● Once you know the number of slices,
check out the price.

● You can now calculate how much it
is per slice. (You may need a calculator
for this bit!)

● Bring all your findings into school.

There are [ ] Slices in a loaf.

The loaf costs [ ] P

So the price of a slice is [ ] P

impact MATHS HOMEWORK

Tea bag tester

● How many cups of tea will a tea bag make before it is 'naught but water'! Test out a tea bag in your house.

YOU WILL NEED: a clothes peg and a tea bag and a tolerant family.

● Make as many cups of tea with the tea bag as you can. Count as you go. Between cups you can peg the bag up!

● Bring your findings back into school.

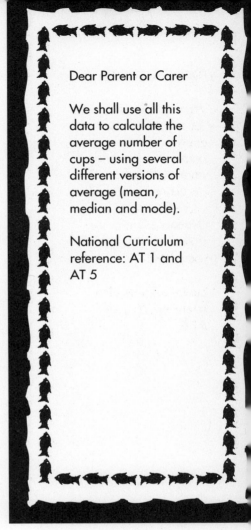

Dear Parent or Carer

We shall use all this data to calculate the average number of cups – using several different versions of average (mean, median and mode).

National Curriculum reference: AT 1 and AT 5

_____and

child

_____

helper(s)

_____

did this activity together

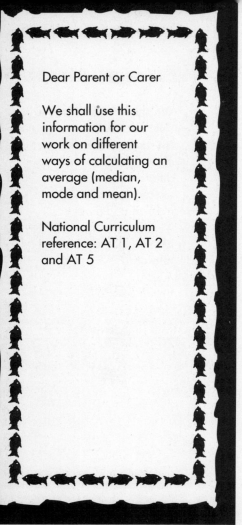

_____and

child

_____

helper(s)

_____

did this activity together

Growth rate

● We all grow at different rates. Can you calculate how many centimetres you grow each year? In order to do this, you will need the help of someone who has watched you grow!

● Using all the information at your disposal, such as old clothes, photos (Where did you come up to on your mum?), actual measurements on a height chart, or anything else you can think of, try to estimate how tall you were one, two, three and four years ago. Go back further if you can.

● Construct a rough height chart in the space opposite for each year. How many centimentres do you think you have grown each year on average?

● Bring your estimates into school.

Small shop or supermarket?

● Do most families shop at the local small shop or at a large supermarket? We are going to carry out a survey to find out.

● Ask as many families as you can – including your own – where they shop.

● You will need to design a data-collection sheet which will allow for the fact that some people may say that they shop at both. Do they do equal amounts of shopping at both? Do they go to the supermarket once a fortnight and the local shop every evening? Do they spend equal amounts of money at both?

● Design your questions and think about how to record your answers. Bring all your information back into school.

Dear Parent or Carer

We shall use all the information the children collect to set up a database using the computer. This will enable us to analyse their data and represent what we have found out using graphs.

National Curriculum reference: AT 1 and AT 5

_____ and

child

_____

helper(s)

_____

did this activity together

_____and

child

_____

helper(s)

_____

did this activity together

Potato peeling

● How long does it take you to peel a potato? How long does it take other people in your house? Who is the quickest? Who is the slowest?

● Have a potato peeling session – make sure it is on a night when you are eating potatoes for supper!

● Time yourselves peeling potatoes and bring all your information back into school.

impact MATHS HOMEWOR

Essential items

● Which pieces of apparatus which help us to do household tasks – such as the washing machine or the vacuum cleaner – do you regard as essential?

● Ask whoever does most of the housework in your house what they think. Do they regard the washing machine as the most essential? Or the iron? Together, put all the items you have chosen in order of priority – from the most essential to the least essential.

most essential

least essential

● Bring your list into school.

Dear Parent or Carer

We shall collate all our information and use it as part of a data-handling exercise in class, representing our data on graphs and analysing what we have discovered.

National Curriculum reference: AT 1 and AT 5

_____and

child

_____

helper(s)

_____

did this activity together

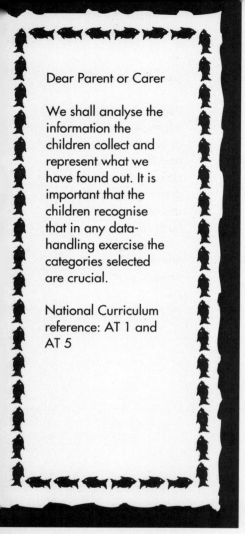

_____and

child

_____

helper(s)

_____

did this activity together

Card search

● What sorts of card can you buy nowadays? Ask someone if you can accompany them to a newsagent's card shop and have a look. What cards do you see? How would you classify them?

● Think about all the different categories into which they might be sorted and make a comprehensive list on the back of this sheet.

● Which sort do you buy most often? Which sorts are seasonal?

● Bring your list into school.

impact MATHS HOMEWORK

Birth pangs!

● At what time of day were you born? See if you can find out. Was it morning, afternoon, evening or during the night? As near as you can, write down the hour of your entry into the world.

● Can you find out when other people in your home were born?

We are conducting this survey to find out if it is true that most babies are born at unsociable hours!

● Bring as much information as you can into school.

Dear Parent or Carer

The children will collate all their data on to a computer database which will enable us to analyse and represent what we have discovered on graphs.

National Curriculum reference: AT 1 and AT 5

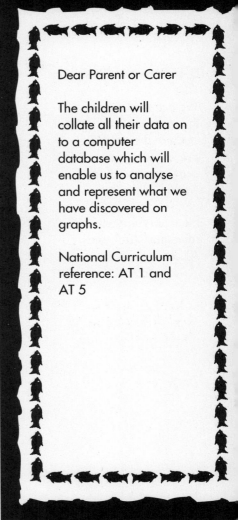

_____and

child

_____

helper(s)

_____

did this activity together

Dear Parent or Carer

We are working on the mathematical study of probability at present and this activity is part of that work.

National Curriculum reference: AT 1 and AT 5

_____and

child

_____

helper(s)

_____

did this activity together

Pascal's probability

The triangle depicted on the accompanying sheet is called 'Pascal's Triangle' after Blaise Pascal. It has a function in helping us to calculate probabilities.

YOU WILL NEED: a coin, a pencil and paper.

● The number of the row tells you the number of coins to spin. (That is: first row, spin one coin; second row, spin two coins; and so on.)

● Add up each row of the triangle – the first ones are done for you. This tells you the number of possibilities there are for the ways the coins might land.

● The actual numbers in that row tell you the actual ways in which it is probable the coins will land.

So if I spin three coins – there are 8 ways they could land (by adding up the third row!):

HHH HHT HTH HTT THH THT TTH TTT

Of these, there is 1 chance in 8 that they will land all heads; there are 3 chances in 8 that two will be heads and one tails; there are 3 chances in 8 that two will be tails and one heads; there is 1 chance in 8 that they will all be tails...

and 1, 3, 3, 1 is the third row!

● Try this out for other rows of Pascal's triangle!

● When you actually throw the coins, does it really work?

impact MATHS HOMEWORK

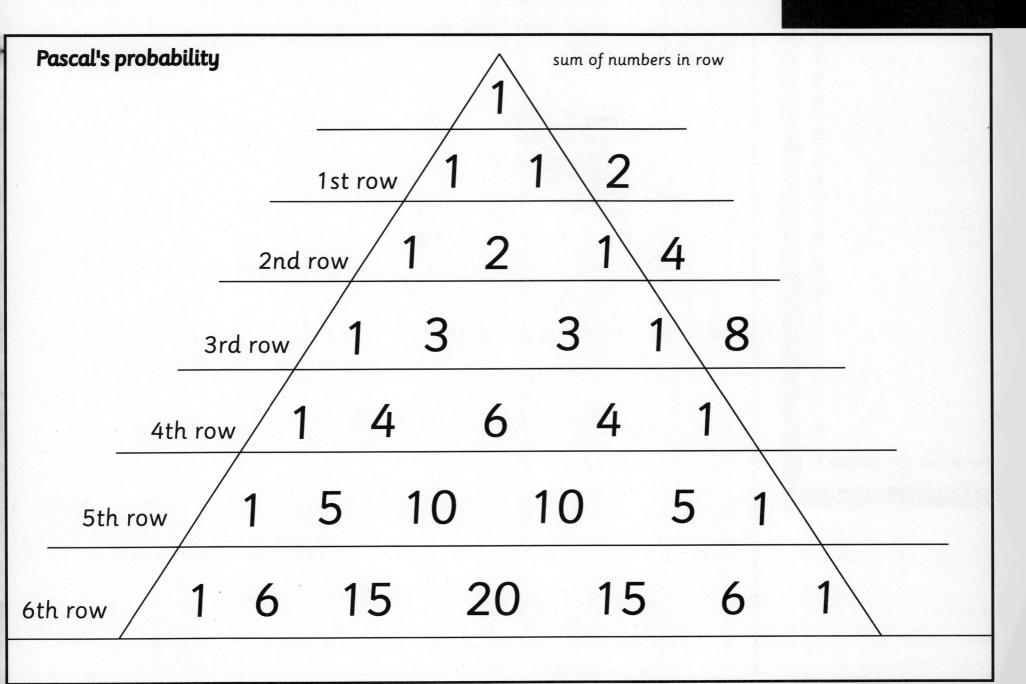

Pascal's probability

sum of numbers in row

1

1st row   1   1   2

2nd row   1   2   1   4

3rd row   1   3   3   1   8

4th row   1   4   6   4   1

5th row   1   5   10   10   5   1

6th row   1   6   15   20   15   6   1

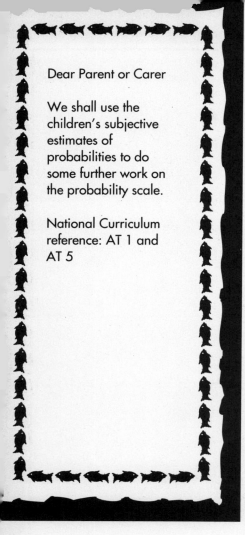

_____and

child

_____

helper(s)

_____

did this activity together

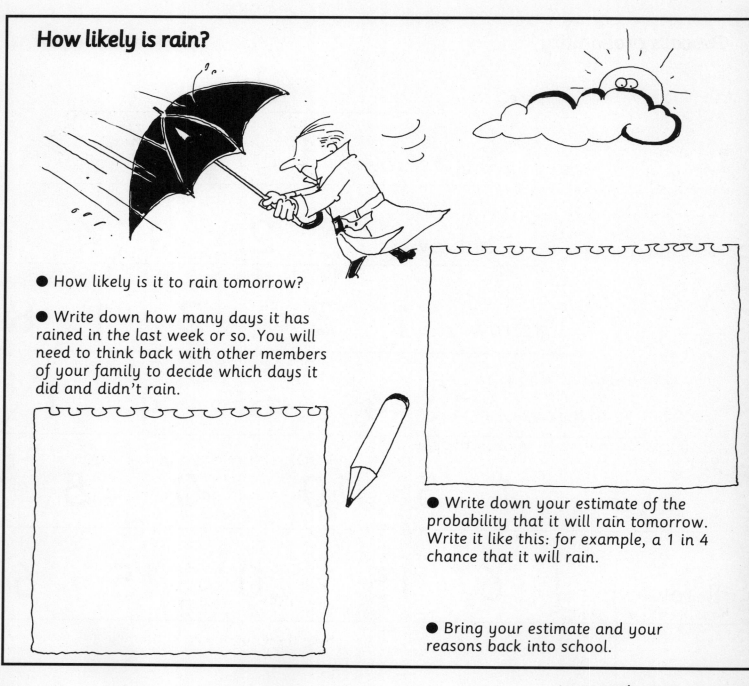

How likely is rain?

● How likely is it to rain tomorrow?

● Write down how many days it has rained in the last week or so. You will need to think back with other members of your family to decide which days it did and didn't rain.

● Write down your estimate of the probability that it will rain tomorrow. Write it like this: for example, a 1 in 4 chance that it will rain.

● Bring your estimate and your reasons back into school.

Cat chances

YOU WILL NEED: a dice, paper and a pen for each player.

● What are your chances of collecting a whole cat in six throws of the dice, if you score as follows:

If you throw a 6 – draw a body (you must start with this!).

 If you throw a 5 – draw a head.

If you throw a 4 – draw a tail.

 If you throw a 3 – draw the front paws.

If you throw a 2 – draw the back paws.

 If you throw a 1 – draw whiskers (the head must be drawn!).

● Play with someone in your family. Take it in turns to throw the dice. Who gets a whole cat drawn first? Count how many throws you each take to get your cat.

● Play several times. What is the average number of throws it takes to get a cat?

● Bring all your scores into class.

_____and

child

_____

helper(s)

_____

did this activity together

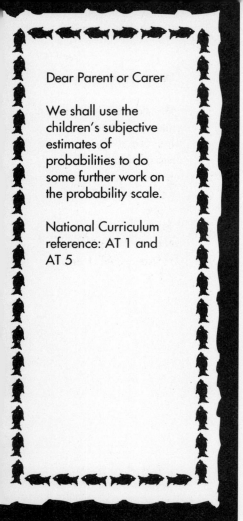
_____and

child

_____

helper(s)

_____

did this activity together

Throw him down the stairs!

● What are the chances of teddy landing on the fifth stair if you throw him down the stairs!?

YOU WILL NEED: a soft teddy which you can throw safely and gently, paper and pencil for your helper.

● Ask someone to help you. Stand together at the top of a flight of stairs. Throw teddy down, but before you do, predict which stair he will land on. Your helper must write down your prediction. Then throw him (not too hard!). Which stair did he land on? Write this down.

● Repeat this ten times.

● Bring all your predictions and scores into school.

Five colours

YOU WILL NEED: eight pieces of card cut out from the back of an old birthday or Christmas card or an old cereal packet. Put a red dot on two of them, a blue dot on two, a green dot on two, a yellow dot on one and an orange dot on the last one.

● Shuffle the cards and lay them in a row face down on the table. Take it in turns with someone to turn over a card. Before you touch it, you must say what colour it will be.

If you are right, score as follows:
Red – 5 points;
Blue – 5 points;
Green – 5 points;
Yellow – 10 points;
Orange – 10 points.

● Leave each card turned over face up and let the next person have a turn. Who wins?

● Is the scoring fair?

● Invent your own game of chance with these cards. Bring it into school.

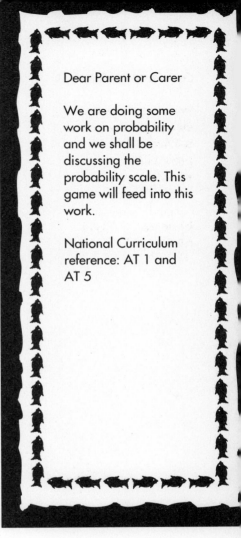

Dear Parent or Carer

We are doing some work on probability and we shall be discussing the probability scale. This game will feed into this work.

National Curriculum reference: AT 1 and AT 5

_____and

child

_____

helper(s)

_____

did this activity together

Roll a letter

YOU WILL NEED: a penny coin, paper and a pen.
● Take it in turns with a helper to roll a penny coin on to the letter grid on this page. Write down the letter it lands on.
● Keep playing until one of you can make a three-letter (or longer) word.

That person should score 3 points (4 if it is a four-letter word). Play again.
● What are the chances of getting a vowel? What are the chances of getting a 'T' or an 'S'.

● Bring all your work into school.

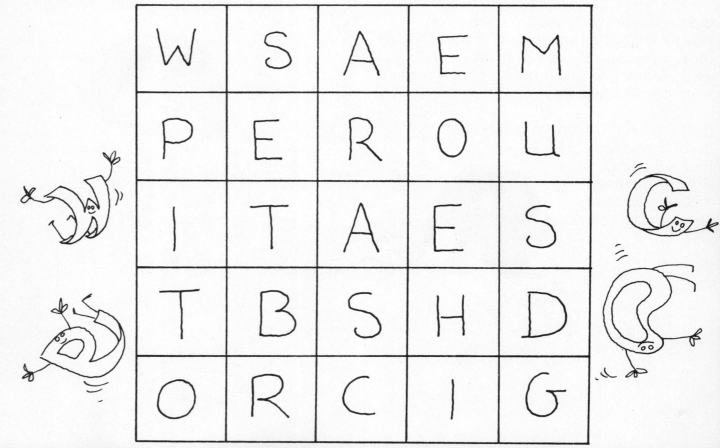

W	S	A	E	M
P	E	R	O	U
I	T	A	E	S
T	B	S	H	D
O	R	C	I	G

impact MATHS HOMEWORK

Coin or dice?

YOU WILL NEED: a pencil and paper, two coins and a dice.

● Take it in turns either to throw the dice or to spin a coin. In either case, you must predict how it will land – heads or tails, in the case of the coin, or which number (1–6) in the case of the dice.

● If you choose to spin the coin, and you are right, score 2 points. If you choose to throw the dice, and you are right, you get 6 points. If you are wrong, you get nothing!

● Play until someone has 15 points or more. They win!

● Is the scoring system fair? Write down why you think it is or isn't.

● Bring your explanation into school.

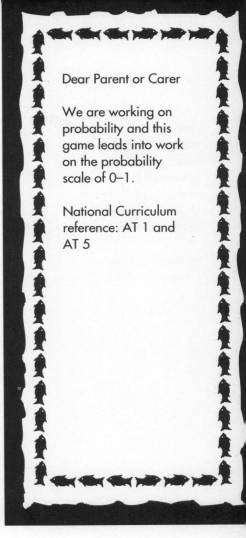

Dear Parent or Carer

We are working on probability and this game leads into work on the probability scale of 0–1.

National Curriculum reference: AT 1 and AT 5

_____and

child

_____

helper(s)

_____

did this activity together

Handling data   125

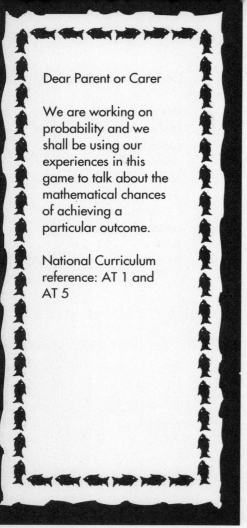

_____and

child

_____

helper(s)

_____

did this activity together

Card divides

YOU WILL NEED: 11 cards (either from a pack or home-made), two sets of 1–5 and one 6.

● Shuffle the cards and deal them out into two piles putting the extra card face down in the middle. Which pile do you think the 6 is in? Together with a helper, decide on a pile.

● Check through the cards. If you were right, deal out another hand.

● If you were wrong, one of you takes the other pile and one gets the single card (take it in turns to do this). Which of you has the 6? If it is the person with the single card, they score 6 points. If it is the person with the pile of cards, they score 1 point.

● Keep playing until one of you reaches 10 points or over.

● Is the scoring system fair? Why do you think it is structured as it is?

● Can you invent your own rules and scoring system?

impact MATHS HOMEWORK

Probability puzzles

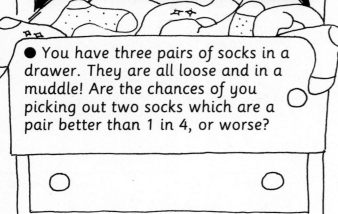

● You have three pairs of socks in a drawer. They are all loose and in a muddle! Are the chances of you picking out two socks which are a pair better than 1 in 4, or worse?

● You are tossing a coin. Someone bets you that it will NOT land heads three times in a row. You have five throws to try. Is this a good bet for you?

● Two children are throwing a dice. One of them throws a 4. What are the chances that the other child will get a better score with his throw?

● How would you estimate the chances of your oversleeping tomorrow?

● Make up some more probability puzzles of your own and bring them into school to share.

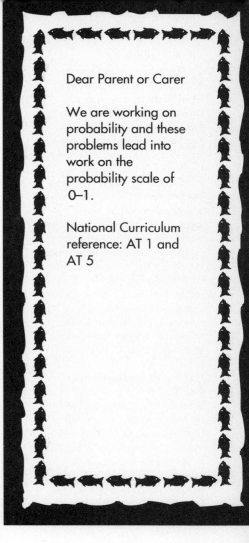

Dear Parent or Carer

We are working on probability and these problems lead into work on the probability scale of 0–1.

National Curriculum reference: AT 1 and AT 5

_____and

child

_____

helper(s)

_____

did this activity together

IMPACT diaries

The IMPACT diaries provide a mechanism by means of which an efficient parent-teacher dialogue is established. Through these diaries, which last up to two years depending upon the frequency of the IMPACT tasks, teachers obtain valuable feedback both about children's performances on specific maths tasks and about the tasks themselves. Parents are able to alert the teacher to weaknesses and strengths and nothing about the child's performance in maths comes as a big surprise at the end of the year or when the statutory assessments are administered. The diaries are a crucial part of this homework scheme.

Help with implementing IMPACT

Schools that wish to get IMPACT started by means of a series of staff meetings or in-service days may like to purchase the IMPACT INSET pack which contains everything that is needed for getting going. This is available from IMPACT Supplies Ltd, PO Box 1, Woodstock, Oxon OX20 1HB.

Useful telephone numbers

IMPACT Central Office (for information and assistance): 071 607 2789 at the University of North London on extension 6349.
IMPACT Supplies Ltd (for diaries and INSET pack): 0993 812895.

Correlation of the Scottish maths curriculum with the English curriculum

The Scottish curriculum is divided into the Attainment Outcomes given below.

(PSE) Problem-solving and enquiry skills

(IH) Information handling

(NMM) Number, money and measurement

(SPM) Shape, position and movement

PSE is the equivalent of the English AT 1

IH permeates the Scottish maths curriculum, in that its requirements apply to all maths activities in NMM and SPM.

English	Subject	Scottish
AT 2	Number	NMM
AT 2	Money	NMM
AT 2	Measuring	NMM
AT 3	Algebra	NMM
AT 4	Shape and space	SPM
AT 5	Data handling	IH

LEVELS

Scottish	English
A	1/2
B	2/3
C	3/4
D	4/5
E	5/6

Correlation of the Northern Ireland maths curriculum with the English curriculum

The Northern Ireland curriculum is divided into the Attainment Targets (ATs) given below.

(AT N) Number

(AT A) Algebra

(AT M) Measures

(AT S) Shape and space

(AT D) Handling data

English	Subject	Northern Ireland
AT 2	Number	AT N
AT 2	Money	AT M
AT 2	Measuring	AT M
AT 3	Algebra	AT A
AT 4	Shape and space	AT S
AT 5	Data handling	AT D

LEVELS

N Ireland	English
1/2	1/2
2/3	2/3
3/4	3/4
4/5	4/5
5/6	5/6

impact MATHS HOMEWOR